TAKING BEAUTY TO THE
NEXT LEVEL

You Can Succeed in Medical Skin Care

TAKING BEAUTY TO THE

NEXT LEVEL

You Can Succeed in Medical Skin Care

CARLY WILLIAMS

Niche Pressworks

Dedication

This book is dedicated to the people who have changed my life and given me this wonderful journey—my clients over the years, who helped to mold me into the esthetician that I am today, and my students, who have trusted me to help shape their futures.

Contents

Foreword

CARLY WILLIAMS IS, FIRST AND FOREMOST, an innovator and leader in medical esthetics and laser technician education. She has extensive esthetician and laser training experience and certifications and has been a speaker and course provider throughout the country for the past decade. Carly was also the first to create a center of training specifically in medical esthetics and the first in the field to register with the Minnesota Office of Higher Education.

She and her staff of advanced practice estheticians and laser educators are doing something no one else in the Upper Midwest has done—providing hands-on esthetic and laser training with an impressive collection of actual lasers and highly trained professionals in a small class setting. Her school, MedSpa Institute of America, not only provides training but also gives its students a definite advantage in this competitive job market. Countless students have benefitted from their time there.

This book is full of excellent advice for starting a successful career in medical skincare. It is well worth the time to read, as it comes from a person who is regarded as a luminary in this rapidly evolving field. I urge anyone interested in a medical esthetics career to take advantage of the information Carly has provided regarding the industry about which she is so passionate. She truly has spent her career working to take the field of medical esthetics to a higher level of excellence.

Richard H. Tholen, M.D., F.A.C.S.
Minneapolis Plastic Surgery, Ltd.
Minneapolis, Minnesota

CHAPTER 1

Planning a Career— the Struggle Is Real

I REMEMBER SITTING AT THE LUNCH TABLE in high school when everyone was talking about where they were going to college or what career they would be in. I knew I wasn't going to go to college. I knew I wouldn't get in, and I knew I didn't want a career where I would have to sit behind a desk and watch the rest of my life go by. None of it genuinely sounded like me. I wouldn't be good at it, nor would it make me happy.

Besides, did I really need college? From freshman year in high school, they put so much pressure on you to start looking at which colleges you might attend, but nobody seemed to want to help the people who don't want to go to college. I don't have anything against college in general. If you really want to go to college, and you need it for the career you've chosen, then you should go that way. However, my hard-working parents did not go to college. My mother is a hairstylist, and my father fixes elevators. So, in my experience, college wasn't necessarily required for a happy, lucrative career. Some careers like those of my parents, which might require trade school but don't involve as much time or money as college-related careers, can have great rewards. So I was already thinking along those lines.

Not knowing what I wanted to do with my life, I felt pressure to just sign up for something. So I tried hair school. However, after a short time, I realized it wasn't right for me, either. The others in my classes seemed to enjoy them so much—but I just didn't feel that way. Realizing this, I got very discouraged.

By that time, I felt super lost. Maybe because of how depressed I felt, I couldn't even make it to class on time. But I kept sticking it out because I did not want to give up.

And then one day, one of our teachers said, "I hate to say this to you guys, but today you will be 50 percent through this program. That means that if you come in tomorrow, you will have to pay full tuition even if you drop out or don't finish. If you don't come in, you only have to pay up until today, so have a hard think about whether this is for you."

That was my sign—I had to commit or change something. I already owed $5K for a program I couldn't even get myself to make it to on time. Why keep spending money on it?

However, hair school did give me a clue about what I did want to do—esthetics. In the program I was in, I really enjoyed the single day we learned facials. I spent $5K to learn that, but at least it got me on the right track.

Going with that hunch, I switched to esthetics school. After that, I had perfect attendance. (Side note: I did not realize how much teachers—and employers—love perfect attendance.) Then, I started seeing the light of hope.

I continued on that path until one day, my dermatologist recommended getting into skin-care lasers. I had had no idea that was even a career, and it sounded fascinating. Plus, I had realized that though I would enjoy skin-care esthetics work, I would still have trouble making enough income. So I needed to add something.

I started looking into adding some medical laser training, but it really did not exist yet. If it did, no matter how much it was, I would have taken it because it was what I wanted to do. Thankfully, my doctor helped me get into her network with lasers after esthetics school, where I did my best to train on the job. And then I started to understand the potential.

I realized that once you get laser trained, you can double, triple, or, like I did, even quadruple your salary as an esthetician. That's when I truly realized you don't need college. You just need training in something that is in demand and will make you a good income. So I went through school on a shorter, less expensive route than college and made great money in the end, anyway.

Once I had improved my skills to the point where I felt I could teach others, I started training friends informally for free in laser skin care to help them get into the field, too. I wanted to help anyone interested in getting into this career.

Pro Tip: Opportunity is Everywhere

Stay open to opportunities—you never know where they will come from. My dermatologist didn't realize the impact she has had on my life until recently. I can't stress enough how important your network is. So many people in the world are willing to help you, especially when you least expect it. Maybe they also can help you get to a route faster—if so, swell! Take the opportunities when they come.

But that wasn't an ideal situation. I was concerned that there were no formal laser skin-care programs in the industry, especially when the skill was in demand. That's when I realized I could start a school of my own that could help train people to work in various esthetics positions and earn viable incomes.

I wanted to create the perfect school, one I wish existed when I was looking for my own answers. It would be a beauty school that intertwined medical aspects. It would offer laser certification, advanced medical machines and tools, medical-grade skin-care lines, and professional career advice, tips, and tricks.

I kept all those things in mind later when I created MedSpa Institute of America.

The same reasoning is also why I am writing this book. I want to help others succeed, and this field holds such incredible opportunities. A book like this didn't exist when I could have used it, but it can now—because I can write it for you. So if you're trying to figure out what to do with your life, and you hate the idea of going to college, this might be the opportunity you've been looking for.

Real Success Is Worth It

Okay, I get it. You probably have doubts. After all, you didn't like high school, and now I'm telling you to try a career that requires school. If you weren't good in high school, and you hated every minute of it, can you really succeed in another school?

Absolutely.

Remember, I had the exact same mindset. So, if I can, you can.

Plus, no one was around to show me the steps to get into the field, clear up my misconceptions, and give me tips on succeeding. But I'm here to do those things for you because I want to see you succeed, too. So, you already have an advantage I didn't.

What do I mean by success? I want to see you have a financially stable job with hours that allow you to be home for dinner and not have to work on the weekends. I value my work-life balance a lot, and this career allows that. Plus, I want you to have the opportunity to set an example for your children and be at all their activities. Being in medical skin care, I can do that—and so can you. You can focus on the things that really matter—whatever yours are.

After being in the field since 2010, I have a lot to share with you. I know what it's like to have no one to help you navigate through all the confusing information and suggestions. So let me give you some things to think about—things I had to find out the hard way.

> *I know what it's like to have no one to help you navigate through all the confusing information and suggestions. So let me give you some things to think about—things I had to find out the hard way.*

Avoid the Income Crunch

Thinking about a new career (or changing your career) can feel intimidating. You have to consider all the choices and their pros and cons. And you also may have to deal with others' expectations that you will just go to college. But if you don't take time to think about it, you'll wind up in a situation that doesn't address all your needs.

Sure, it's great to have a career doing something you like or even love, but shouldn't you be paid enough to live a decent life while doing it? As I looked into just plain esthetics when I was in cosmetology school, the average income was between $20-30K, and I had made more than that as a waitress. I didn't have to go to school to be a waitress, so the added investment didn't seem worth it.

Independence Gives You Security

When you are eighteen years old, you have no understanding of money. I lived at my parents' house. I had no idea how much a house or car payment was, not to mention home and car insurance. And don't forget groceries, daycare, gasoline, your water bill, your gas bill, your electric bill, your health and dental insurance, Internet service, phone service, pet costs, gifts, clothes, going out, and everything in between—the list goes on and on. When you add all of that together, $30K is not much money. I did not realize how hard it would be to live on that kind of income. A good dose of reality definitely makes you appreciate your parents.

As I started adding all of this up, I began to panic. I thought, "If I don't meet a rich man soon, I am in trouble!" Okay, I'm mostly joking, but who hasn't had that cross her mind in that kind of situation? But to be honest, I didn't want to be relying on others anymore. That's why I wanted to move out of my parents' house. With a career in medical esthetics, I could succeed on my own.

Take a Different Mindset—Cost vs. Investment

And then there's the cost issue. Many people don't have the money to go to college and don't want to take out a loan, especially when they have no idea what they even want to do quite yet. But they also might think it's better not to spend money on schooling of any kind. Why bother? They're not going to do well anyway, and all that money would be wasted.

But that's only one side of the picture. Look at my situation. Sure, I would have wasted money on beauty school to train in hair, which I wasn't good at and didn't like. But, if I had succeeded in the program, the training would have basically locked me into doing something I hated so I could pay back my schooling.

On the other hand, spending money on something I loved, which would make me a lot of money, was totally different. It blew my mind that to invest just $10K in medical laser esthetics, I could double what I would have made with just the beauty side of esthetics. And I would double it not only that year but *every year for the rest of my life*. That is a no-brainer. That's also when I started to understand the concept of investing money to make yourself more money. It's not just about making a lot of money but about making life a little easier. And let's face it: If you can pay your bills and save some money or invest it toward your kids' college and your retirement, your life will be easier.

> *It blew my mind that to invest just $10K in medical laser esthetics, I could double what I would have made with just the beauty side of esthetics. And I would double it not only that year but every year for the rest of my life.*

The Information Can Be Confusing

As I mentioned before, I wrote this book because there isn't much information out there about this career. There's also some conflicting information.

The medical and beauty sides of esthetics are often lumped together, but they're not the same. For example, an esthetician's license from a cosmetology school doesn't qualify you to work in a medical office. Unfortunately, doctors don't consider a beauty license to be the proper training to operate lasers.

Laser certification gives you a lot of information and training in safety (for both you and your client) and other aspects that you need to know before working on a live person without supervision. That's essential because you *will* be working without supervision—the doctor won't be in the treatment room with you. If you don't understand how to use the equipment safely, you won't be comfortable. Good clinical esthetics programs also teach things like charting so you can work in a doctor's office—traditional esthetics doesn't cover this.

Plus, think about this. If you do get hired to work on lasers without a laser certification, is this an employer you want to work for? How would you feel if you were a client going in for a laser-related procedure, and you learned that your esthetician had no formal training or certification in lasers? Yikes. That's probably how your client would feel, too.

THE DATA DILEMMA

Some of the information about estheticians vs. medical estheticians can be confusing. For instance, as of this writing, Beauty Schools Directory showed outdated information on its website from 2018 US Labor Statistics for medical estheticians. The median hourly wage of $19.35/hour in a physician's office, compared to $13.73 for healthcare settings[1], was not current. The actual link to the US Bureau of Labor Statistics pointed to more recent data from 2020, showing higher salaries[2] —but you wouldn't know that without clicking on the link. In addition, this type of information doesn't always include commission-based pay as part of the wage calculations. So the hourly wages in some positions would naturally be lower because the commission is higher. And finally, instead of

1   "Esthetician vs. Medical Esthetician: What's the Difference?" Beauty Schools Directory, accessed May 15, 2021, https://www.beautyschoolsdirectory.com/programs/esthetician-school/esthetician-vs-medical-esthetician

2   Bureau of Labor Statistics, "Occupational Outlook Handbook: Skin Care Specialists, Pay," US Department of Labor, updated May 2020, https://www.beautyschoolsdirectory.com/programs/esthetician-school/esthetician-vs-medical-esthetician

separating the medical side from the beauty side, industry data often lumps them together, bringing the average for medical esthetics much lower than is accurate.

Always look for data from 2020 or later because prior to that, the industry was still grouping both the medical and beauty sides together despite their vast differences. The statistical resources are still catching up as the industry evolves.

Fear and Doubt Can Paralyze You

When it came to school or work, I felt stuck in the headspace of "I can't do it." That seemed odd because I didn't feel that way with things that scare others, like sports, speaking to large groups, or meeting new people. I was great at making new friends and networking.

To overcome my self-doubt, I had to understand where it was coming from. Eventually, I realized that I'm a very hands-on learner, and the traditional school environment wasn't my forté. I had a fear of dealing with abstract stuff like math or spelling big words. I felt I wasn't very smart. Tests freaked me out. I didn't even bother taking the state's college admission test because I was so terrified. I can't be the only one who's felt that way! And, of course, homework would give me terrible anxiety, which is ironic because here I am, writing this book—a giant homework assignment I gave myself. But that just shows you that anything is possible if you set your mind to it.

I finally realized my strengths: I'm a very social person with good street smarts. I'm not awesome at traditional school, but that doesn't mean I'm not smart. I'm just smart in a different way. Until I got rid of my labels for myself, I didn't think I could achieve a medical esthetics career. So that's what I urge you to do—think differently and be willing to push yourself.

Ask yourself this: How are *you* smart? What are *your* strengths? Everyone is smart in his or her own way—including you. You just have to decide to see it instead of being afraid or believing your own labels for yourself.

Everyone is smart in his or her own way—including you. You just have to decide to see it instead of being afraid or believing your own labels for yourself.

If you are already in an esthetics-related career, you might doubt what I'm saying. Would shifting to medical esthetics really be better? After all, you've taken a lot of time to build your clientele. You don't know if you can do it, whether you will like it, or whether the effort will be worth it. You're already familiar with your current job, and learning something new is intimidating.

But you've picked up this book for a reason. Why? Do you like your current career, or are you looking for a change? Do you feel you are totally satisfied, or do you want more? If you do want more, you're going to have to take a risk. Otherwise, you'll never know whether you could do it.

Every day you don't try is a day of your potential new life, gone. How many more days, months, and years are you willing to lose?

CHAPTER 2

Medical Skin Care Will Change Your Life

SO WHY IS MEDICAL SKIN CARE SUCH A GAME-CHANGER from being in a spa or salon? The easiest way to show you that is to tell you about a past student I had.

Jenny is a single mom of five. She worked at a gym during the day and bartended at night to make ends meet. Her most important goal was to spend time with her family, but her work situation did not allow her to do that.

Jenny got certified on lasers through our course and took a leap of faith to start her own spa in a tiny town. (Side note—opening a business in the middle of nowhere can be a great thing with no competition.) She started by providing quality foot baths in a room at a chiropractor's office. Then she slowly started adding other services, such as facials and microneedling.

Within only six months, she had so many clients that she needed to hire a second person to help handle all the work. Seeing how lucrative and flexible Jenny's career was, Jenny's daughter also invested in laser training and started working alongside her mom. Eventually, they moved out of the chiropractor's office into their own suite, with their own reception area and treatment rooms. Jenny set up her own front reception desk and hired a couple more employees—including another of her daughters.

Jenny is now with her family all the time, which is what she truly wanted. She was fortunate enough to afford a laser, which eventually gave her the ability to attract so many clients that she now has three locations in total.

Buying an $80K laser may seem like a significant investment. However, the large profits from laser-related services enable you to make much more money, more quickly. For example, in the same amount of time, you could either do a $2.5K laser treatment...or a $20 eyebrow wax. Which would you choose if you're making a commission from both of them? There's no comparison.

Jenny also recently purchased a second piece of equipment and is on the hunt to buy her own building, with dreams of making it more than just a spa. I can't share her goals because they're confidential at this point, but I am excited to watch it all unfold.

Eight Reasons to Start Your Career in Medical Skin Care

I've brought up some reasons this career gives you so many opportunities, but let's talk details.

#1: You'll Have Better Work-Life Balance

Jenny's story shows that it's possible to succeed if you put your mind to it, which applies to anyone. Laser certification allowed me to buy a car and house when others my age were just starting college. Now that I have a daughter, it has set me up for a blessed life where I can work from 11 a.m. to 5 p.m., be home for dinner with my family, and have the weekends free. It's exciting to be home when my husband gets home from work. My schedule also allows for attending my kids' sports or outside activities. I can even be there for my husband's beer league baseball games, where we make memories with friends.

If you work at a regular spa, they usually are open until 9 p.m. You're lucky to head out by 9:30 p.m., and you would have to work every weekend for the rest of your career. It's great if you don't mind that—but if you do, it should factor into your career decisions.

#2: You'll Have Exciting Career Options

Medical laser certification can give you more business opportunities than a regular beauty school esthetics program can. Here are some kinds of places you can work:

- A dermatologist's office

- A plastic surgeon's office

- A laser company, either as a trainer or as a laser salesperson

See Chapter 4 for a more detailed list.

Medical esthetics training expands your opportunities within the industry network. For example, a sales representative selling a skin-care line would make a lot more money selling medical skin-care products than a regular spa line. Medical product prices are much higher, and the effects are longer lasting.

According to 2020 data from the US Bureau of Labor Statistics, the esthetics industry is predicted to grow over the next decade by a whopping 17 percent. That's way above the average of all occupational growth, which is only 4 percent.[3]

#3: You Can Do More for Your Clients

When you work at a regular spa, you are doing facials, waxes, peels, needling, tinting, dermaplaning, etc. Unfortunately, these things not only don't make you as much money as medical laser and other treatments, they also don't get long-term results for the client.

I can't tell you how many times clients have told me things such as, "I don't like my veins here," or pointed out unwanted age spots, acne scars, etc. Unfortunately, if you aren't laser-trained, you have to send clients elsewhere to fix these things. It gets frustrating when you can't truly help them with their concerns. But if you add laser training on top of all the other services you provide, you don't have to send them anywhere else. Your more extensive menu of services means a bigger paycheck for yourself, sure—but also less running around for your client.

If you're already in esthetics and love your clients, you owe it to them to get the training and tools to give them the results they need. If you're sending them elsewhere, you risk losing them. If they can get all the services they need somewhere else, they'll go there, no matter how much they like you.

---

3   Office of Occupational Statistics and Employment Projections, "Occupational Handbook: Skin Care Specialists/Summary," US Bureau of Labor Statistics, May 2020, https://www.bls.gov/ooh/personal-care-and-service/skincare-specialists.htm#tab-1

#4: You'll Have More Work Variety

Just doing facials, waxing, and lash tinting all day can get very routine, which is why people get burnt out and change careers.

The more techniques and skills you master, the more variety you will have in your job. As a result, you won't feel like you're doing the same thing repeatedly every day, and you won't get burnt out nearly as quickly.

#5: You'll Have Higher-Quality Clients and Easier Sales

Laser treatments cost a great deal more than beauty-side esthetics. Therefore, laser skin care attracts a person who is already at least partly aware of the types of treatments and is ready to spend a larger amount of money to solve their issue quickly and permanently. Selling to and educating this type of client is just easier. You won't have to convince them to do something; they are usually already looking for solutions you can provide.

#6: Medical Esthetics Is a Secure Industry

During the initial three months of the COVID-19 crisis, our industry was shut down along with the whole US. But in the end, we still thrived. Did things slow down? Of course. Some people avoided contact longer. Every client is different. Even with such essentials as food, some people had groceries delivered to their homes much longer than the initial risk period while others were packed in the grocery stores through the whole situation. The same was true for the esthetics industry. But our industry, which relies on clients being personally present for treatments (you can't deliver a laser treatment), still stayed afloat. The fact that people still wanted to spend the money on laser procedures during the COVID concerns shows that many people view this business as a necessity. Stability during crises makes it a great career option.

#7: You'll Work in a Positive Culture

Everyone has the stereotypical image of the hairdresser knowing everyone's business in town—or the salon where the clients sit and gossip. Many salons can have fun, upbeat atmospheres, but some don't.

Doctors' offices are the opposite. They almost always will have a positive atmosphere without a lot of drama and gossip. So, if you prefer a drama-free work culture, you will like working in a doctor's office.

In a doctor's office, the culture is professional. There is too much going on for gossip or cattiness. You are too busy and have to focus on what you are doing, or things can go seriously wrong. Doctors have too much on their plates with surgeries and other treatment aspects to care about drama.

Also, the teams in doctors' offices are smaller than at spas and tend to know each other well. This is because doctors' staff members don't often leave; they stay and grow, mastering their jobs and moving up. In my experience, salons have higher turnover than medical offices, especially if the salon culture is negative or the pay is low. Again, not all salons are like that. At some, especially those with a coaching program culture, people stay until they open their own suites. But on average, salon staff stay only three to five years in any given salon.[4]

#8: Medical Esthetics Is Easier on Your Body

When you're young, you may not think physical stress will matter. But over time, tasks that are hard on your hands and body can take a toll.

---

4   Reach, "Minimizing Stylist Turnover," Octopi Commerce LLC, February 21, 2020, https://octopi.com/minimizing-stylist-turnover-2020/

When I was only doing beauty-side esthetics, massaging people hurt my hands and wrists after a while. And doing a lot of facials one after another required me to hunch over in a way that eventually caused back pain. Though I was young and could handle it, it would get a lot harder over time.

It's not uncommon for massage therapists or other estheticians to have to change careers for this very reason. They just can't take the physical stress on their hands and bodies after a while. For instance, massage therapists often have to leave their careers early—on average at the age of forty-three—due to repetitive stress injuries from performing their work.[5]

These are professionals trained to relieve injuries. If they have issues just from standing all day or working in awkward positions, it makes sense that people in trade or factory jobs that require a lot of bending and lifting would, too. The jobs may pay well, but when your body starts to break down, what will you do?

Medical skin care is ergonomically easier on the body, and it doesn't require heavy labor. Even if you do keep your ergonomically challenging job part-time while doing medical skin care, you'll find that breaking up your other work with laser treatments that don't involve massage or force you to be in awkward positions will give your body a break.

Numbers Talk

I've given you a lot of general information, but now, let's do some math.

Let's say you are a medical esthetician with a mix of laser and non-laser services. To simplify things, let's say you only have one

---

5   Andrea Picincu, "Hazards of Being a Massage Therapist," *Houston Chronicle*, September 25, 2020, https://work.chron.com/hazards-being-massage-therapist-14144.html

client sale per day for each of the following services (which is much less business than you would usually have).

To calculate what you'd make each day/month, you would first need to calculate the amount of your commission. To figure out what that would be for a month, you'd multiply that amount by twenty since you'd only be working on weekdays, and there are about twenty weekdays per month. Then you just have to multiply the month's total by twelve since there are twelve months in a year. So the calculations look like this:

AVERAGE COST PER TREATMENT		
Treatment	**Average Charge Per Sale**	
Eyebrow Wax:	$20	
Microneedling:	$300	
Laser Underarm Hair Removal:	$1000	
Photorejuvenation Laser Treatment:	$2500	
COMMISSION CALCULATIONS		
Treatment	**Commission**	**Earnings Per Sale**
$20 Eyebrow Wax	60%	$12
$300 Microneedling	40%	$120
$1000 Laser Underarm Hair Removal	20%	$200
$2500 Photorejuvenation Laser Treatment	20%	$500

If you provide these sales for one month, for twenty weekdays only, you will make:

EARNINGS EACH MONTH		
Treatment	**Calculation**	**Total Per Month**
Eyebrow Wax:	(20 sales x $12)	$240

Microneedling:	(20 sales x $120)	$2400
Laser Underarm Hair Removal:	(20 sales x $200)	$4,000
Photorejuvenation Laser:	(20 sales x $500)	$10,000
	Total:	**$16,640**
EARNINGS EACH YEAR		
Treatment	**Calculation**	**Total Per Year**
Eyebrow Wax:	(12 months x $240)	$2880
Microneedling:	(12 months x $2400)	$28,800
Laser Underarm Hair Removal:	(12 months x $4000)	$48,000
Photorejuvenation Laser:	(12 months x $10,000)	$120,000
	Total:	**$199,680**

That would represent one client for each service each day. Imagine if you had a fully booked day with different clients and additional services I haven't even mentioned! Just adding a laser could add an extra $2.5K a month to your pocket or an extra $30K a year on top of your microneedling treatments.

Of course, like any job, you will have your good and bad days, busy and slow months, but it evens out to a salary that can bless your life.

I didn't come from money, and though some people assume my parents helped me fund my business, they didn't. Honestly, I didn't tell my parents anything about my business in the first couple of years. I didn't want them to worry about the sacrifices I was making to build it. I truly was able to start it because of the money I made as a laser technician.

Think about that. I didn't just make money doing this. I started an entire business, all by myself.

Now It's Your Turn

Now it's time for you to do some of your own math.

1. What do you currently earn each year (before taxes)?
    _____

2. How many hours do you work each week to earn this amount?
    _____

3. Do you have to work more than one job to make ends meet?
    _____

4. How much do you spend each year on general expenses?
    _____

5. Does any of that have to go on credit cards because you don't
    have the money? _____

    If so, how much? _____

6. Now, suppose that as a medical esthetician, you could earn
    $50K/year working only weekdays. Is that more money than
    you earn now? _____

    If so, subtract your salary from $50K to find out how
    much more: _____

7. Now, let's be a little more ambitious. If you could make more—
    say, $60K—would that be more than what you make now?

    If so, subtract your salary from $60K and write that
    amount here. _____

8. Now divide the amount you wrote in #7—the difference between
    what you're making now and what you might make—by 12.

This is how much more per month you would make. What would you do with that extra money each month?

_____

9. Let's think about the next five years. If you just save that extra money each year, how much would you have? Multiply the amount you wrote in #7 by 5. _____

What could you do in five years if you could just save that money over those years?

10. It's not only about money—time is important, too. If you're working more than 40 hours/week, subtract 40 from the number of hours you're working now, and write that total here:

_____

What would you do with that extra time each week?

_____

Through the previous sales scenarios, I've already shown you that making $60K is very possible (it's not guaranteed, of course, but it is truly possible, and especially if you follow my other tips). Now you have an idea of what it could mean in real dollars compared to what you make now or hope to make in your career.

But guess what? Those numbers you just added up are only a little higher than average. That means there are people in this industry making a lot more.

In fact, what if I told you I made between $20K and $50K per MONTH—not per year—when I worked for a doctor?

I can't guarantee you'll earn that kind of money, but if you work hard and have a professional attitude, you can earn a great income.

STATISTICS

According to Salary.com, as of May 2021, the average clinical esthetician salary in the US was $48.6K/year[6], which equates to $23.36/hour for a full year of full-time work (2080 labor hours). Laser-certified estheticians will make more than this, as this data is not segmented by type of training/treatment.

Noting that industry data is often averaged together for both types of estheticians, Vocational Training HQ reported that medical estheticians, especially those in doctor's offices, earn higher salaries than their non-medical counterparts, with an average of $48,990 as of 2013.[7]

6   "Clinical Esthetician Salary in the United States," Salary.com, updated May 27, 2021, https://www.salary.com/research/salary/alternate/clinical-esthetician-salary

7   "How to Become an Esthetician: The Definitive Guide," Vocational Training HQ, accessed May 15, 2021, https://www.vocationaltraininghq.com/how-to-become/esthetician/#Salary

CHAPTER 3

Clear Your Misconceptions

WHY DO WE ASK THE WRONG PEOPLE FOR ADVICE? For example, why do we go to a single friend rather than our married friends for relationship advice? Why do we ask our partners for career advice when they don't know our field?

Even those in the industry can't necessarily give you good advice if they aren't keeping up with trends. The esthetics industry is changing. The people who went to beauty school twenty years ago don't necessarily know what's going on today. They may mean well but give advice based on their own misconceptions.

If someone isn't informed with current facts about something, they probably can't help you make a good decision. In fact, a lot of misconceptions about the esthetics industry in general—sometimes by estheticians themselves—often lead to incorrect assumptions about medical esthetics.

Traditional And Medical Esthetics
Are Not the Same Industry

Beauty-related skin care and medical skin care may seem similar, but they are truly two different worlds, two different networks, and two different sets of jobs in general.

If you're looking for advice on the medical side, get it from medical vs. beauty-side skin-care professionals. No matter how good a person's intentions might be, beauty-side estheticians likely won't have good information about the medical side—and vice versa for medical-side estheticians.

If you're looking for advice on the medical side, get it from medical vs. beauty-side skin-care professionals.

Also, always evaluate the advice you're getting based on the person's success and demonstrated knowledge within the industry he or she is advising about. Attitude also counts—seek out people who love their industry and what they do. If you find someone you want to switch lives with because they have an awesome job, good income, and lots of happy clients, that person is definitely doing something right.

On the other hand, be wary of people who will try to talk you out of getting into a field they don't work in. I had some situations where people on the beauty side told me I wouldn't make any money in medical skin care—and this turned out to be completely wrong. They meant well, but they didn't know the real facts though they believed they did. Listening to them would have been a terrible mistake. In situations like that, you can appreciate and thank the person for their good intentions without being obligated to follow the advice. It's important that you weigh it against more credible information.

Medical Esthetics Schools Differ from Traditional Programs

When you evaluate schools, you may hear this argument from well-meaning people: "Just pick a school. They all teach the same thing anyway, so what does it matter?"

But that's not true.

Most beauty schools are hair or cosmetology schools that have skin care on the side as a program that doesn't get as much attention. At MedSpa Institute of America, we pay 100 percent full attention to *only* skin-care services. We do not offer hair or other traditional beauty training. The reason is that we built our curriculum for the people who want to end up in medical spas, dermatologist's offices, or plastic surgeons' offices.

That's why MedSpa Institute is the first school to create a formal laser certification program. We are the pioneer of medspa training in the Midwest. We were also the first to introduce clinical aspects into our programs. For instance, we teach things such as how to assist a dermatologist vs. a plastic surgeon. This helps students see where they would belong since the two jobs are not the same.

> *We truly changed the industry, offering something that never existed before—laser and clinical beauty programs under one roof.*

We truly changed the industry, offering something that never existed before—laser and clinical beauty programs under one roof. It's the program I wish existed when I was first starting!

Not only do regular beauty schools only teach an older curriculum, but the teachers usually do not have experience with advanced esthetics or medical devices. They cannot give proper training or advice to prepare students who want to go into medical esthetics, just as MedSpa Institute instructors can't provide training in traditional cosmetology.

Therefore, always look at a school's curriculum carefully. Are they preparing you for your true career goals?

You Do Need Formal Laser Training

One of the most common misconceptions people in traditional esthetics have is that you don't need formal laser training to do laser treatments. "You will learn to use lasers on the job," they tell people who are interested in this career.

Unfortunately, this is not good advice at all, for several reasons.

First, most doctors do not know how to operate their own lasers. They cannot teach you. If no one else on their staff knows how to do these treatments, how will you learn?

And second, even if a coworker does train you, how do you know she is doing the technique properly? You would have no experience to judge.

Advice against formal training made sense before 2010 when we had no other training options. However, the lack of formal training meant we all learned some things wrong. That was exactly why there were so many burns in the industry, and lasers had a bad reputation. I trained my friends because there were no other good options—but that wasn't a great scenario, and I would never advise anyone to do that today. There's no reason to, because there are far better options today, and people should be aware of them.

That's why nowadays, as I mentioned, it is a serious red flag if someone is okay hiring you without training. What does that say about the clinic? If they aren't on top of the industry standards for safety and technique, what kind of service will they give?

Sixteen Lost Months

One prospective student came in with her husband to MedSpa Institute for an informational tour. They were well informed and ready with great questions. During our session, I learned that others had told her not to waste her money on laser training; she wouldn't need it. She admitted that she was going to try to get a job without the laser training just in case.

"Do whatever feels right," I advised.

Sixteen months later, they were back for another tour, during which she told me that after six months of job applications, she had had no interviews. She wanted to work in a legitimate office with high ethical standards, and those offices wanted trained estheticians. Other places where she didn't want to work didn't mind hiring her, but she realized how poor her training would be and how unsafe it felt to go there. She wanted a real career and a legitimate job in this field. She just had to see for herself how to get there.

You Don't Have to Be a Nurse

Another common myth is that you have to be a nurse to do laser skin-care treatments. This is true in a couple of states, but most don't require a medical degree.

Even in nursing, you aren't taught laser theory, which is why even nurses and doctors have taken this course as well. Someone with a medical degree doesn't necessarily know laser theory and how to operate machinery. You don't need nursing or physicians' credentials to operate it properly—but you do need the proper training.

...But You CAN Be a Nurse

Obviously, if someone has both a nursing degree and laser certification, they are a golden nugget for employers —or maybe a unicorn. But because it's just not required in most states, you can still make a similar salary since a lot of lasers are commission-based vs. hourly. So despite the expensive nursing degree, the nurse will make the same commission as you per treatment. The regular pay a nurse would make doesn't factor in. But to do the same job, the nurse still needs the same credentials you could get without a nursing degree.

One of my graduates is a nurse who didn't want to do typical nursing in a hospital or similar environment. Instead, her dream was to be a registered nurse esthetician. She now owns a business and office suite, has her own clients, and does injections and treatments full-time.

Another nurse graduate works part-time at a hospital and part-time at a medspa. She likes both jobs, as they are each different. And she can work super part-time at both and still make good money.

Good Information = Better Decisions

I hope you can see now why it's so critical to seek advice from people in the right industry before deciding whether this type of career is right for you or how to move forward. With that in mind, the next chapter will show you what types of careers you could have as a medical esthetician.

CHAPTER 4

Career Potential

A BIG ASSUMPTION IS THAT YOU WILL JUST GET HIRED to work with lasers as a laser tech. But there's much more to this type of career than laser skin care. Different job environments will change your day completely, and what happens between the lasers will make (or break) your dream job.

Let's chat about all of the different career options.

1. Medical Spa Esthetician

A medical spa differs from a regular spa in that it offers cosmetic medical services in a spa-like atmosphere. That means it is overseen by a physician, which helps to guarantee the staff are well trained and highly skilled and the treatments are safe and effective. Medical spas can do anything from laser hair removal or laser skin rejuvenation to chemical peels and vein treatments.[8]

---

8   Stephanie Kies, "What Is a Medical Spa?" Blanchard Valley Health System, accessed April 23, 2021, https://www.bvhealthsystem.org/expert-health-articles/what-is-a-medical-spa

Pro Tip: Look Beyond the Label

Keep in mind that many places may use the term "medspa" in their company name, but that doesn't mean they are a true medical spa. To evaluate this, check for two things:

1. Is a doctor on staff overseeing the treatments? If not, it is not a true medical spa.

2. Do they offer medical-grade treatments? A place calling itself a "medspa" but only offering lashes, peels, and facials is not a true medical spa. A true medical spa will use medical devices such as lasers and offer medical-grade peels, which are different types of peels.

TYPICAL DAY: As an esthetician at a medical spa, you'll be handling many types of procedures, some of which don't involve lasers. Your day in this position could be totally random; each client could have a different type of need. For instance, you could have a laser hair-removal appointment, then a tattoo removal, followed by a stretch-mark removal, then another laser hair removal, and so on. This variety makes the day fun, and it goes by quickly. You'll be doing procedures on your own rather than assisting a doctor.

JOB PERKS: Unlike at a dermatology office, you would not be assisting anyone. This means you can focus your time on your own clients and earn commissions for the entire day.

2. Dermatology Esthetician

Dermatologists are medical doctors trained specifically to diagnose and treat conditions related to hair, skin, and nails.[9] This is a

---

9   Kimberly Holland and Sara Perkins, "What Is a Dermatologist and How Can They Help You?" *Healthline*, June 24, 2020. Accessed at https://www.healthline.com/find-care/articles/dermatologists/what-is-a-dermatologist

different environment from a medical spa. Medical spas can help remove blemishes and improve cosmetic appearances, but they don't diagnose or treat skin diseases or disorders.

Not all dermatologists use newer devices such as lasers, so not every dermatologist will be hiring laser-trained estheticians. You may have to look around a bit to find the ones who are passionate about up-and-coming types of treatments.

TYPICAL DAY: As you might expect, working as a medical esthetician for a dermatologist focuses much more on the clinical/medical aspects of the business. Since the doctor is always there to overview the procedures, you have added assurance that they are done well. Also, multiple doctors usually work together in one office, which means there's a lot of medical oversight with high safety and treatment standards.

You'll be working with your own clients, doing treatments such as chemical peels, microneedling, microderms, laser hair removal, and photorejuvenation treatments (if the facility offers laser treatments). When you don't have a client, you will often be helping the doctor log patient information and doing other things.

JOB PERKS: You'll be working closely with dermatologists and helping gather patient information related to many skin issues. This will help you learn a great deal about different aspects of medical skin care, such as the nature of different skin diseases and conditions.

3. Plastic Surgery Esthetician

My personal favorite job opportunity is in plastic surgery. Unlike dermatologists, plastic surgeons expect you to know what's going on because they're in surgery all day and have limited time to answer your questions or oversee your treatments. Plastic surgeons look for staff who want to stay around for a long time, who are confident in the treatments they are offering, and who can sell for the business.

TYPICAL DAY: A plastic surgeon's office is generally a smaller team of people with minimal turnover. In this field, doctors need your help with a lot of different tasks. You'll operate the treatment machines, do consultations for the specific surgeries the office offers, handle patient intake and discharge paperwork, and answer patients' questions via phone while they're healing. You'll also do patient post-care, checking in on their healing, taking out stitches, and assessing their general progress. In this job, patient charting is crucial.

The clientele in a plastic surgeon's office consists of people getting a wide range of treatments. They could want optional cosmetic improvements such as reducing the effects of aging. Or they might need vital surgery after a disfiguring accident or a health issue such as breast cancer. Plastic surgery patients tend to be more upscale and can afford their procedures even if not covered by insurance.

JOB PERKS: If you like a job with freedom and flexibility, this is a great fit. Doctors are doing surgery all day and give you independence in handling your time.

4. Laser Trainer

As a laser trainer, you work for the laser company in addition to your regular employer, so it's a great opportunity for extra income. Plus, you get to travel across the US and Canada. With the chance to examine all the equipment and see how it is made, you will get to know the product in-depth and become highly expert in its use.

The laser company whose equipment I used at my first job asked me to become a laser trainer for them. They flew me to the location where the lasers are made and trained me in detail on all the equipment. This experience made me realize how important it is to understand how lasers work, so you don't hurt somebody.

TYPICAL DAY: You will usually have a couple of states that are considered your territory. New accounts purchasing a laser can purchase a four- or eight-hour training session with the company. This is very basic training that covers how to put the laser together and clean it. The company gives the option to the pool of trainers, who get to choose who will train them. So if you don't want a particular assignment, you don't have to take it.

Your clients are people in laser treatment centers who will be using the new equipment to do the treatments for their own clients. You will need to be able to travel on short notice, as you usually have a two-day window to accept a training appointment. Since you're doing training work on top of your other work, you also need to make sure it's all right with your main employer. At the time, I had no kids and was in a flexible job, so it was easy for me to take training requests.

JOB PERKS: Being laser certified and a trainer will give you an advantage over others for higher-paying positions. And you'll have a lot of options for doing training because laser companies are always looking for laser trainers. They want people who are also in the field and continuing to practice lasers. It's a great opportunity if you like to travel, network, and meet new people—and it's all paid for by your employer.

5. Laser Sales

Going into laser sales is also an option. Not all companies require a college degree to be a medical laser sales rep. You just need to know how the machine works and how to sell it.

Having experience using the equipment benefits you in sales. Being able to describe how the equipment works in real settings helps you connect with potential clients. This gives you an advantage over a college graduate with a sales background but no experience with that kind of equipment.

TYPICAL DAY: As a medical laser sales rep, your clients would be companies that use the lasers for medical treatments. These include medical spas, dermatologist offices, plastic surgeons' offices, and smaller licensed facilities with laser-certified staff doing cosmetic treatments. You would travel a great deal to help new clinics get set up and on their feet. You also need to stay in touch electronically with people who have questions about the machines as they are setting up or making decisions about what to purchase.

Ask Yourself...

When deciding on a career, most people consider the skills they would need. However, they often forget to think about other things, such as the environment, lifestyle, and flexibility they would prefer. For example, all of the esthetician jobs I've mentioned involve different amounts of pressure, income levels, travel requirements, and hours. When you know what appeals to you and how you're motivated, you'll make better choices about the best career for yourself.

When you're evaluating your options, ask yourself questions like these:

- What are my strongest skills? What careers would use these most?

- What are my weakest skills? Would the careers I'm interested in require them as a top priority, or could I figure out how to work around my weaknesses?

- Do I prefer to be home for dinner, or do I like working in the evening?

- Do I mind working on the weekends?

- If I already like what I'm doing but am thinking about more income, could I add laser procedures to my skill set and menu? If so, how? Could I work part-time at what I'm currently doing and part-time doing laser treatments to make more money?

- What kinds of procedures would I enjoy doing? What would I prefer not to do?

- Do I like interacting with people and helping them directly, or am I more interested in the skin care part of the job—doing the procedures and solving cosmetic problems?

- Is there anything I'm scared or unsure about? Am I open to trying it to see if I might be good at it and like it?

There's More to a Career than Money

Though money is important, you could make a lot of money but still not be happy in a career if you forget about other types of rewards. Here are just a few:

- Helping people solve problems so they can feel great about themselves—and sharing in their happiness.

- Being on a professional team whose members all work well together and support each other's goals.

- Gaining new skills and knowledge on the job.

- Meeting interesting people.

- Getting to travel to interesting places for work as a laser sales rep or trainer.

- Being considered an expert in your field.

- Having some control over your day.

- Gaining confidence from doing things you never believed you could do.

- Being appreciated for the hard work you put in and the results you bring to your team.

If any of these things sound good to you, you would definitely enjoy a career in medical esthetics.

Pro Tip: Pride Yourself on Your Professionalism

Medical esthetics is a professional career—not just a job. Doctors and staff take what they do seriously. Things like showing up on time aren't optional; they're a must. If you're late for one appointment, every appointment afterward will be late, too. That will throw off your whole day and frustrate patients—and doctors don't want unhappy patients. If you're aware of how you present yourself and support your team as a professional, it will pay off in great working relationships with your employer, your co-workers, and your clients.

CHAPTER 5

Choose Your School Wisely

AS I MENTIONED PREVIOUSLY, the medical laser industry has changed a lot over the last decade. Lack of good training in the past caused the field's reputation to suffer due to safety and other issues. But that has all changed. In addition, new types of equipment and techniques are continually being created, requiring more training.

All of this created the need for laser operators to learn things the right way and keep advancing their skills. As a result, training evolved and became more formalized. The industry also created better standards and ensured people had to meet specific skill and knowledge requirements to become certified to operate the equipment. As these things happened, safety issues due to untrained staff and less effective equipment or riskier techniques have slowly disappeared, and industry credibility has grown significantly.

Part of being a professional is taking pride in the safety and effectiveness of the industry itself. That means doing your best to support its reputation through your own quality work.

This is why taking a job in the field without any training isn't just a massive risk to others; it also doesn't do the industry any favors. Part of being a professional is taking pride in the safety and effectiveness of the industry itself. That means doing your best to support its reputation through your own quality work.

Think about it this way: Do you want a career you are proud of, in a field you are also proud of? Or do you just want a job that will make you some money but won't really give you any achievements or skills to take pride in? The people who succeed in their fields get satisfaction and pride in doing what they do well, which is an excellent reward beyond money.

Finding the Right Program

Since you're still reading this, I hope that by now, you've decided you want to explore medical esthetics training programs to see what might work for you and what they offer. But what do you look for during this process?

Start with your chosen field/fields

Think about the careers that sounded most interesting to you from Chapter 4. You'll want to research to find schools that offer types of training to prepare you for them. For example, if a school you're researching doesn't provide laser certification, it probably isn't a candidate for medical esthetics training.

Compare Important Facts

These might vary a little based on the type of field you want to get into, but in general, here are some things to look at:

- **Licensing:** Is the school licensed within its state? Does it offer certification in the programs that require it?

- **Job placement statistics:** What percentage of the program's graduates get jobs, how soon after graduating, and where?

- **Average graduate salaries:** What kinds of salaries do the school's graduates earn after one year, and after five years?

- **Esthetics program variety:** Does the school offer a good variety of programs and training in case you want to change your focus or add new skills to what you've already chosen?

- **Supplemental training:** What kinds of additional non-esthetics training, such as sales/marketing, networking, interviewing, etc., do they offer to help you succeed in your career?

- **Instructor credentials:** What kinds of backgrounds do their instructors have? Do some have experience in the career you are interested in? That's a bonus. They will be able to give you lots of insider tips and may know people who can help you find a job.

- **Facilities:** (You may not be able to get a sense of this without a tour.) What are their facilities like? Would you feel comfortable in the classrooms? Do they have newer equipment to train on?

- **Program Quality:** Are they up to date on the latest techniques? Do they offer lots of hands-on experience to get comfortable with the equipment? If not, how will you get enough experience on it to feel confident in your skills?

- **Class Sizes:** Are the classes small enough that you'll have a lot of personal time with your instructors for questions and mentoring, or so large that you'll just be one of a crowd?

- **Career Assistance:** What kinds of opportunities and assistance do they offer to help you find a job after you graduate?

- **Flexibility:** Are their classes/schedules flexible if you'll be working while going to school?

- **Reputation:** What kind of reputation does the school have in the industry? What do employers say about the school's graduates? Do employers seek out those graduates specifically due to the school's reputation?

- **Financial Assistance:** Do they help students plan strategies for financing school? Do they offer any financial assistance?

Tour Your Top Choices

Once you have narrowed down your selections to two or three schools, you should schedule a tour to get a better idea of what the facilities and people are like and whether you can picture yourself there.

As you're doing your tour, think about the learning process. Obviously, you'll be training on equipment and learning new techniques. But what if you're struggling with a particular topic? Do they have people to help you? What kinds of people will you have as your classmates?

Also, pay attention to the network of the people you would be surrounded by. Do your instructors know people working in the places where you want to work? Do they have connections that can help you meet more people to find more job opportunities?

Everything in life is about who you know. The best basketball player in the world will never get signed on for a professional team if no one knows who he is. The same goes for you.

Here's an example: Suppose you want to work in a medspa. Medspas are going to reach out to a medspa school to hire people, not the traditional beauty schools that only offer esthetics and/or hair. Or, if you specifically want to work in a dermatology office, and the school you attend isn't as well known in that field as others, you will most likely not have as many opportunities for networking there.

Suppose you want to work in a medspa. Medspas are going to reach out to a medspa school to hire people, not the traditional beauty schools that only offer esthetics and/or hair.

Also, keep in mind that doctors using the latest techniques and equipment will want to hire people who know how to use them. If the school you attend has outdated or limited equipment, doctors will probably recruit from other schools with more up-to-date training.

Your School Is an Investment, Not a Cost

It might seem logical to start looking at costs right away to find the least expensive school, but just looking at the price doesn't give the whole picture.

It's better to think of your schooling as a long-term investment, not a cost. A cost is something you just pay to get something of supposedly equivalent value. But an investment is money you put toward something that will (you hope) give you a much bigger payoff than your original investment. In other words, the value you receive for your investment will be much larger than the investment itself.

Key Things to Compare

Obviously, with any school, you want to get the most for your money. So how do you know what kind of return you're going to get? It depends a lot on the training the school offers—because that directly affects the kind of career and pay you can get once you graduate. That's why it's good to compare the facts listed in the "Compare Important Facts" section—placement rates, salaries, etc.—to get a better idea of the school's performance. Of course, these things are not a guarantee because your success also depends on your own work and the current market. However, knowing your chosen school's general performance gives you a good idea of how it stands up against the competition. You can also calculate possibilities for yourself using other students' average return.

Licensing

This is critical. If a school is far less expensive than others but isn't properly licensed to train in lasers, are you actually "saving" money going there? Sure, it might be far cheaper, but what kind of training will you get? What type of job are you going to get when you can't answer the interview questions correctly? If you do get a job, how long will you keep it if you accidentally burn clients because you aren't adequately trained to operate the equipment?

And finally, if a school is training people in lasers without certification or licensing, you should question their ethics and any factual information they give you about themselves. It would be wise to speak with reputable individuals in the industry who hire in that area to see what they say about the school.

Hands-On Experience

You will want as much hands-on experience as possible while you're in school. The more you can train with lasers and other equipment/products, the better. At MedSpa Institute of America, the opportunity for hands-on training is infinite—and I'm not kidding. You can do as much of it as you want! The whole point of getting hands-on experience is to feel comfortable starting in a place where others most likely won't be able to help you or answer questions. If your classmate needs five times to do a technique before getting comfortable, but you need ten, why should you be limited to the amount of time your classmate needs? Everyone learns differently, and some techniques might be more challenging for different people to master than others. Each student should have time to learn at his or her unique pace.

Industry Connections

Another critical thing that will stand out with reputable schools is their number of industry connections. At MedSpa Institute, our network is massive. We have relationships with many vendors, skin-care companies, and skin-machine companies—in fact, many work exclusively with us because of our reputation and level of success. Due to these relationships, many medspas prefer our graduates and reach out to us to help them with hiring. This gives our students an advantage in making the connections they need to get jobs.

We have some exclusive contracts with companies stipulating their specific techniques will only be taught at our school since I am the trainer for our state. In addition, we have teachers who are also either trainers for devices or skin-care lines or own their own businesses. So we can provide exclusive training not only in laser techniques but also in the business itself.

Program Variety

Being able to attend a school that offers many different types and levels of knowledge, such as esthetics, advanced esthetics, laser skin care, injections, microblading, and so on, helps students get exposed to everything so they are informed in general and can make better decisions about what they want to do most. For example, our beauty students get to watch a demo of how injections are done, so they at least know the general technique. Even though most aren't nurses and therefore won't be doing that treatment, they'll still be able to answer clients' questions about the treatments and can help sell them.

All of this translates into knowing more about what's out there so that you can make a better decision. And, learning newer devices and being up to date on the latest machines will help you get that higher-quality job. Doctors always want what's new, and we deliver. You need to make sure that whatever school you choose will give you the variety of exposure and training you need to meet their expectations.

MedSpa Institute Placement and Salary

Good training is one reason why MedSpa Institute graduates consistently outperform the average industry salary and career placement for medical esthetics. Our graduates consistently make around $40–$50K on average, compared to other schools' graduates, who make $20–30K after graduating. Our students more frequently get jobs at medspas or doctors' offices, while graduates of other schools work at smaller waxing centers or small spas.[10]

---

10   Per data gathered by MedSpa Institute of America as of May 2021.

Examples of Programs

To give you an idea of what medical esthetics training is like, I'll tell you about MedSpa Institute's curriculum.

MedSpa Institute is the only doctor-run medical esthetics school in Minnesota with state-of-the-art skin-care science. This means we train in the correct medical practices within our clinical school. We have set the standard for the skin-care industry in Minnesota and were the first to offer not only laser training but even advanced training in skin care and devices through programs exclusive to our school. The state beauty board is working hard to keep up with us because they haven't heard of some of the new technology. When these advanced skills and treatments eventually become industry standard, our graduates will already know how to do them.

The following are some training programs MedSpa Institute offers.

Luxury Laser Procedures

The MedSpa Institute laser training program is an intensive, two-week program, during which students learn techniques and get to practice supervised treatments on each other. The institute continually updates its training on laser and other high-level skin-care equipment. Techniques include:

- **Removal of unwanted blemishes:** Lasers can be used to safely remove tattoos, cellulite, freckles, scars, veins, unwanted hair, etc., from the skin.

- **Body and facial skin tightening:** Some lasers can send heat deep into the skin without harming the top layer, tightening the skin from within. According to the

American Academy of Dermatology Association, laser resurfacing (an intensive treatment of this type) is the most effective non-surgical procedure for tightening loose skin.[11]

- **Teeth whitening:** Laser whitening offers several advantages over peroxide whiteners. For instance, lasers can focus on specific areas that are more discolored than the others, unlike just using a general whitening tray.[12]

- **CoolSculpting®:** This is a non-invasive treatment that removes fat cells in specific areas. Unlike other treatments such as liposuction, CoolSculpting uses freezing temperatures to break down and remove the fat cells without damaging the skin or other tissue—no surgery needed. It has been shown to remove up to 28.5 percent of the fat from targeted areas.[13]

- **CoolTone®:** This treatment uses magnetic muscle stimulation (MMS) to strengthen and tone muscles. One treatment can be far more effective than several trips to the gym, with minimal effort or side effects.[14]

---

11 "Many Ways to Firm Sagging Skin," American Academy of Dermatology Association, accessed April 30, 2021. https://www.aad.org/public/cosmetic/younger-looking/firm-sagging-skin

12 "Laser Teeth Whitening: How Does It Work?" Dental.net, accessed April 30, 2021, https://www.dental.net/cosmetic-dentistry/laser-teeth-whitening/

13 Zawn Villines and Cynthia Cobb, "Does CoolSculpting Work?" Medical News Today, June 8, 2018, https://www.medicalnewstoday.com/articles/322060#research

14 Kelly Wale, "Cooltone vs. CoolSculpting: What's the Difference?" Westlake Dermatology, November 23, 2020, https://www.westlakedermatology.com/blog/cooltone-vs-coolsculpting-what-is-the-difference/

- **Photorejuvenation:** This type of treatment uses light-based equipment to tighten and renew the skin's appearance and lessen the signs of aging.[15] MedSpa Institute teaches techniques using laser technology.

When you evaluate a school, try to research the current industry techniques for the career you're interested in and then look at whether the school offers training in them. If not, it may be out of date. Also, ensure the program offers a large variety of current equipment to train with.

Look Beyond the Laser Training

You also want to look at what you get with your laser training. MedSpa Institute's laser program also offers the following benefits and added training:

- Certification/Diploma by the state

- HIPAA (Health Insurance Portability and Accountability Act) and OSHA (Occupational Safety and Health Administration) Laser Safety Officer Certification

- CPR (cardiopulmonary resuscitation) and AED (automated external defibrillator) certification

- How to assist a doctor

- Marketing strategies

- General information on how injectables work

---

15   Rebecca Small and Dalano Hoang, "Photorejuvenation with Lasers," Clinical Gate, updated on February 26, 2015, https://clinicalgate.com/photorejuvenation-with-lasers/

- Interviewing skills

- Assigned mentor to help train you

In a program featuring laser training, always ensure that you will receive certification and licensing according to the state where you'll be operating your business. Also, look for benefits such as marketing training, mentors, lots of practice time, and especially safety training! If your program doesn't have these components, it may not give you enough well-rounded skills.

Pro Tip: High Standards Are Better

Look for high standards from your instructors and your school. Yes, they will be tougher, but that's ultimately a good thing for you. MedSpa Institute has an intern program that allows people who went to a different school to intern with us if they can pass a basic test in medical laser operation. No one—not even an intern—should be operating lasers in situations where they could create safety issues without being able to pass this very basic test. This is another reason for our high reputation within the industry.

If the school has high standards, you'll get better training, and if they also have programs to help you succeed, you'll be able to meet those higher standards and get a lot better return on your investment than if you choose a school with easier requirements and lower quality training just to get credentials.

Luxury Esthetics

Seek out programs that offer high-level skin-care training in the latest techniques. For instance, some of the things MedSpa Institute offers in its Luxury Esthetics program include:

- In-depth training in advanced skin care

- Facials

- Waxing

- Lash and brow tinting; lash perming and extensions, and brow henna

- Makeup

- Essential oils

- A state-of-the-art kit including makeup, medical-grade skin-care products, extractor tools, bowls, brushes, a mannequin head, and a lash kit.

Again, these are always being updated as the industry changes and adds new techniques. Note that these techniques include medical-grade skin-care products, which are a level above the products used in the traditional beauty industry.

Luxury Advanced Practices

These practices include medical-grade techniques using the latest equipment and treatments. They include:

- **Microneedling:** A technique to rejuvenate skin by using tiny needles to create punctures in the top layer, improving the skin's texture and appearance. The technique has proven benefits and is popular with celebrities such as Gwyneth Paltrow and Naomi Watts.[16]

---

16   Kathleen Mulpeter, "What Is Microneedling?" Health.com, April 6, 2017. https://www. health.com/beauty/what-is-microneedling

- **Carboxytherapy (exclusive to MedSpa Institute):** A treatment using carbon dioxide infusions to remove cellulite, stretch marks, and dark circles under the eyes. It originated in the 1930s in French spas.[17]

- **Dermaplaning:** This procedure uses an exfoliating blade to remove the upper layers of skin (mainly dead skin cells and hair) from the face, helping smooth fine wrinkles and things such as acne scars. It helps the skin keep a youthful appearance.[18]

- **High-frequency facial treatments:** Salons use high-frequency machines to tighten and stimulate the skin and to prevent hair loss. They can balance oily or dry skin, improve skin color, and help tighten sallow skin.

- **Medical-grade chemical peels with Glytone (exclusive to MedSpa Institute):** Like dermaplaning, medical-grade chemical peels remove layers of damaged skin cells but use chemical treatments instead of a blade. These treatments are performed by doctors and can be done at various levels of depth—superficial, medium, or deep.

- **Advanced extractions:** Techniques for removing pimples and blackheads using a needle tip without leaving scars.

17   Ana Gotter and Deborah Weatherspoon, "What You Should Know about Carboxytherapy," *Healthline*, September 18, 2018. https://www.healthline.com/health/carboxytherapy

18   Kathryn Watson and Cynthia Taylor Chavoustie, "Everything You Want to Know About Dermaplaning," *Healthline*, March 27, 2019, https://www.healthline.com/health/beauty-skin-care/dermaplaning

- **BB Glow Semi-permanent Foundation (exclusive to MedSpa Institute):** A treatment that infuses the epidural layer of skin with a serum that works like makeup foundation, smoothing skin tone and blemishes but lasting seven to thirty days.

- **LED light therapy:** This can be used for several treatment types; different colors of light can treat different conditions. Because LED light does not contain ultraviolet rays, it is safer for regular use.[19]

- **Plasma Fibroblast Therapy (Exclusive to MedSpa Institute):** This treatment uses a pen-like device to discharge a high-frequency electric current to small areas of the skin, treating wounds and helping maintain skin firmness and tightness.[20]

Luxury Injection Training

These courses require a registered nurse degree (or higher) and include medical procedures such as:

- **Neurotoxins:** These injections are to treat wrinkles and other signs of aging.

- **Fillers (face/lips/hands):** These injections focus on filling out sagging areas in the face or other high-profile areas to make them plumper and more youthful.

---

19   Kristeen Cherney and Debra Rose Wilson, "LED Light Therapy for Skin: What to Know," *Healthline*, April 5, 2019, https://www.healthline.com/health/beauty-skin-care/led-light-therapy

20   Rachel Nall and Catherine Hannan, "What is Plasma Fibroblast Therapy?" *Healthline*, January 17, 2020, https://www.healthline.com/health/plasma-fibroblast

- **Platelet-Rich Plasma (PRP) Injections:** These treatments stimulate the growth of new cells and promote healing. Doctors use them to treat hair loss and repair torn tendons and other injuries.[21]

Luxury Microblading

Microblading is the process of cosmetically tattooing specific areas such as eyebrows and lips to fill them in more. Some of the things taught in the MedSpa Institute course include:

- General microblading and shading

- Business and insurance setup

- Consent and liability forms

- Marketing training

- Info on creating a resume for the tattoo industry or for renting your own suite

The course offers 200 apprentice hours, as well as a kit of pigments and practice skins. Students also receive mentor support and lots of one-on-one training.

The preceding examples show you what kind of coursework is out there—and keep in mind that it's changing all the time. There are always new training opportunities to expand your skills. If you're excited about what you've seen so far, read on for some tips on how to succeed in school and your career.

---

21   Rachel Nall and Elaine K. Luo, "What is PRP?" *Healthline*, September 3, 2018, https://www.healthline.com/health/prp#purpose

CHAPTER 6

Secrets for Success

BEFORE GIVING YOU SOME TIPS FOR SUCCEEDING in this field (both in school and after), I want to talk about something else: negativity. It can really bring you down, especially if you start believing negative things about yourself.

Three Negative Perspectives that Will Work Against You

Working with students and speaking at different schools around the country, I get to know many of the main fears that keep people from trying in this field. Here are three of the most common ones and tips for re-thinking them.

1. "I don't feel qualified to operate state-of-the-art laser technology or do medical-grade skin care."

First off, no one is qualified to operate laser technology until they go through the training to learn how. That's why people get certified. So this concern doesn't make sense. It's basically deciding you're not qualified to get qualified. Don't make the mistake of thinking how you feel before training is how you will feel after.

Also, what do you feel would make someone else a better candidate than you? Are you basing your "qualification" on things that have nothing to do with operating lasers or doing medical-grade skin treatments? For instance, are your ideas of how capable you are or your past failures impeding you? Those things have nothing to do with how successful you can be—unless you let them.

Challenge your way of looking at yourself. If you truly decide to do something and put in the work and the time to learn, you can succeed. Unrelated things from the past don't matter. This is something new. If I can do it despite being a straight D student in high school, you can do it, too.

I can teach students how to use lasers or handle medical-grade skin-care treatments. However, the students are the ones who have to develop the confidence to feel qualified to use them. You can do that if you try—but you won't do it if you have already decided you can't.

2. "I'm a shy person. I'd be uncomfortable selling my services or working with doctors or patients."

If you're shy, that's totally fine. Believe it or not, but you can learn how to not be shy in certain situations. I've had students who've done it. Ever heard of being an extravert in your job but an introvert in your personal life? It's possible.

Focusing on your shyness will only hold you back and can negatively affect your whole life. According to *Psychology Today*, shy people often report difficulty meeting people and making new friends. As a result, they suffer from loneliness and depression. Sometimes other people even think the shy person is rude or standoffish. However, the opposite is true—they desperately want to talk but are just nervous.[22] If these things are holding you back, could it be time to do something about them?

According to *Psych Central*, the key to overcoming shyness is to do things that develop confidence. Those include trying new things (even if you're afraid of them), being mindful, and just acting like you're confident even when you don't feel it.[23] One way to build your general confidence is to be knowledgeable in your field. When you feel like you're helping people and enjoy seeing their results, you won't even think about being shy. You'll be focused on the great results you're getting for them, and your success will build your confidence even more.

Once you get confident in skin care, that confidence might spill over into other situations, too. If you never challenge your idea of yourself, you'll never find out what you can really do.

Pro Tip: Don't Let Fear Limit You

As a medical esthetician, you will have sales goals. Doctors aren't salespeople—it's your job to take that off their hands. The average low-end goal is $10K a month in laser or skin care sales. I usually hit between $20K–$50K a month when I worked for a doctor.

---

22   Bernardo Carducci and Philip G. Zimbardo, "The Cost of Shyness," *Psychology Today*, November 1, 1995/Reviewed May 6, 2020, https://www.psychologytoday.com/us/articles/199511/the-cost-shyness

23   David Shanley, "7 Ways to Overcome Shyness & Social Anxiety," *PsychCentral*, May 31, 2015, https://psychcentral.com/blog/7-ways-to-overcome-shyness-and-social-anxiety#1

If doing that scares you, think about this: If you are in a career you love and you have the right training—including help learning how to do marketing, sales, time management, and the other things you'll need in any good career—all of these can and will become second nature. I've seen the shyest people become sales experts, and you can, too. Don't let fear hold you back!

3. "I've never been good at school. This can't be any different."

I've worked with many students who didn't do well in school in general, whether it's high school or middle school, or maybe a try at college. But they still went on to surprise themselves by succeeding in laser skin care. Why?

What if the whole experience is different? For instance...

What if learning could actually be fun? It can! Something about being in medical esthetics makes learning easier in general. It isn't like most school courses, mainly because it's incredibly hands-on. A lot of people who fail in school are actually just not good abstract learners. They're great at learning things by doing them, but they don't absorb knowledge by just sitting in a lecture listening to someone talk. If you're really a hands-on learner, you can succeed in medical esthetics courses. Sure, you'll have to read some things. However, they will make way more sense when you're interacting with the equipment and processes instead of trying to envision them in your head. A preference for hands-on learning can be a strength in the right kind of learning environment. If you learn how to make the most of that strength, you will totally amaze yourself with the results.

What if learning wasn't boring? When you're actively doing something, you won't be bored. In this case, you'll be practicing techniques, handling and taking apart the equipment, and interacting with people one-on-one or in small groups where you're a part of the lesson. Even when someone else is practicing a technique on you, you're still interacting with them and learning from what they're doing.

What if the program was targeted and didn't take as long? In a program like ours, you don't take a bunch of different courses throughout the week, like in high school and college. Instead, you take intensive, short courses one at a time. These focus on teaching you every aspect of one subject. The course won't last a whole semester; it will last a few weeks. You don't have to try to understand multiple subjects all at once.

What if you get to decide what you want to learn? You get to pick which courses to take at MedSpa Institute of America—depending on what skills you want to master. As a medical esthetician, you can start out with one set of skills and go right into a job, then expand your training to new techniques later, whenever you want to. You are in control of the experience. No one is making you learn things you aren't interested in, unlike most traditional school experiences.

What if you want to keep learning? Ok, that's a joke, right? Why would you choose to keep going to school? How can you do that while also working? Nope, it's not a joke. Continuing education options allow you to keep working while learning new skills. You can never have too much continuing education. I'm considered an expert in my field, and I am still learning new things. New techniques and devices are constantly coming to the market, and I want to know all about them to bring them to my students! If you're passionate about helping people, you will be excited about new ways to do what you already love.

Five Keys to Success

In this field, if you commit to the process and listen to the people who are trying to help you, you can have a great career. Here are five essential tips that can make or break your success.

1. Put your strengths and goals to work for you.
2. Make your own decisions.
3. Respect the basic requirements.
4. Take ownership of the learning process.
5. Create your own "pro networking team."

These things may seem simple, but it's incredible how many people don't understand how important they are. And if you don't understand their importance, you will miss a lot of opportunities. The following sections describe them in more detail.

Put Your Strengths and Goals to Work for You

Looking back on my career, I know part of my success has come from knowing my strengths. For instance, I have a lot of common sense, and it's easy for me to talk to people—but it took me a while to realize those things are just as important as being "school smart." In some fields, they are far more critical. I know my strengths and how to use them, and you can learn how to use yours, too. You probably have more strengths than you know. Strengths come in lots of forms, not just book smarts. Even the desire to make people happy is a strength.

When I hire new staff, I look for genuinely good people—they are happy for other people and approachable. These are strengths. I also look for people who have stayed with one employer for long periods because loyalty and dependability are strengths. If you know your own strengths and your life goals, you will be clear about who you are and what you are trying to do—for yourself and others. You'll also know how to work from your true strengths instead of someone else's idea of you or what you "should" be or do. You'll know which advice to listen to and which to reject or set aside because it doesn't mesh with the real you.

Sitting down and looking at your goals is also vital to get what you want in your life and for your family. If you haven't thought about or written down your goals, how do you know what you're trying to achieve? And how can you make any good plan to achieve it?

There's no perfect way to put together your goals, but I suggest you write them down and keep them somewhere where you will see them frequently. Use whatever system makes sense for you and inspires you, whether it's focused on goals for tomorrow, a month from now, six months, or a year—even the next ten or twenty years. Most people have a mix of both long- and short-term goals.

You may not know what your longer-term goals are yet, but even a general goal of success in a career you love that supports your family is enough to start planning the next six months.

You can break your goals into detailed categories such as personal, family, or wellness goals. You can even set goals for where you want to move or toys and gadgets you want to have! And of course, the categories would include business or professional goals. As you understand more about your field, you'll eventually create specific goals. These could be things like having a certain number of clients, making a certain income, or being at a particular job level within a specific timeframe.

Make Your Own Decisions

One reason goals are important is that they help you make decisions. When you have your goals right in front of you and know what you're striving for, you'll base your life decisions on them. You are the one in the driver's seat, and you have a road map and a destination. You get to decide which road to take to get there.

What do you do when you're not sure whether one route is better than another? For your own life path, you can ask others' advice, but you need to follow your gut about whether or not the advice is right for you. This is such a big piece of advice, and it's not always easy to explain. It's something you just have to start sensing for yourself and practicing to get better at it. That starts with trusting yourself and paying attention to how you make decisions and whether they end up being good ones or not. Then you can start seeing where you go wrong and keep from doing that in the future.

It isn't about avoiding mistakes—it's about owning them and learning from them. After you start trusting yourself to learn, and if you have a clear idea of what you want to do and what you value, you'll get better and better at knowing what's right even when the map isn't clear. It may feel weird because the "knowing" is not even in your head, and it's not in your heart—it's just a feeling or a sense of being pulled in a certain direction, and you just know that's what you're supposed to do at that time. I've had many times when I should have followed my gut and didn't, and things went wrong even though it seemed like I was making a "good" decision when I looked at it from a practical viewpoint. Time and time again, I have had to prove to myself that my gut has my back. So now, I always follow my gut, even when it doesn't seem to make sense at the time. Eventually, it will.

Respect the Basic Requirements

Being a student is not just about learning new technology and getting experience on the devices. Sure, those things will help you succeed, but the other side of your success is learning some simple things that you need to know as a professional out in the field. We have some student requirements that are meant to help prepare you in this way, too. If you can't master them, you'll have a hard time succeeding as a professional. These things include showing up on time, wearing the proper uniform every day, following the requirements for having your hair up, etc.

They seem small, don't they? But they're important. Your teachers are there to teach you everything within a certain time-frame. When you come in late, you aren't respecting them or their time, and you're basically communicating that you aren't committed to the program. They take that into account when they're teaching you. It's not a great investment of their time to try to teach someone who doesn't seem to want to be there to learn. Also, when you get a job, your employer will expect you to show up on time and be there every day. If you can't do that in school, you're less likely to do that in the workplace.

The uniform and hair requirements are there for a reason, too. You'll most likely be required to wear the uniform required by your employer. Again—if your teacher has to tell you over and over that you are wearing the wrong shirt or that you can't wear certain shoes, or that you need to put your hair up, it's a sign that you don't respect the program. Your teachers take that into account, too. If you forget or don't understand right at first because you're new, that's one thing—but if it happens several times, it sends a message.

The rules aren't difficult to follow. Frankly, if a student can't follow simple rules in school, it shows the teachers that they won't be able to follow the rules out in the field either. Teachers are serious about helping students succeed and get jobs. Not only do the teachers want to invest their time helping serious people who come to learn and be positive, but they also want to help employers in their own network find good staff. They wouldn't want to recommend a student who can't follow basic requirements. No teacher can help someone who doesn't want to help him- or herself, and employers don't want to deal with them, either.

Take Ownership of the Learning Process

Forget everything you learned (and hated) about studying. Like I've mentioned, in this kind of program, you learn by doing. Since you usually have to practice with others, it's a great opportunity to get to know your classmates and develop your skills at the same time, both of which are fun! Forget sitting around trying to absorb everything just by reading it or watching someone else do it.

You also learn by asking. You can ask your instructors whatever questions you need to ask. The classes are small, which makes asking questions less intimidating. Even if it is still kind of scary, if you don't ask, you won't get the answer.

Plus, you get to practice as often as you want. So if you don't feel like you're getting something, you can keep doing it until it makes sense. You will learn what you decide you want to learn, and if you take ownership of getting the understanding, you'll be much better prepared for interviews and the day-to-day responsibilities of your job.

Create Your Own Pro Networking Team

Once you've set professional goals for yourself, you will understand more about what kind of network you want to develop. But sometimes, the idea of networking seems weird, like talking to strangers and trying to get them to notice or help you even though you have nothing to give in return.

But that's not what real networking is about, and real networking doesn't have to feel weird at all.

First, though you may not realize it, everyone you know and meet is potentially part of your network. Ask yourself, who would you want in it? Start out by looking around you. Think about what you do every day. Think about who you hang out with and how they act. Do they fill up your cup? Are they there for you? Do they help you achieve success? Do they support you? Do they take you to the next level? Your network creates opportunities for everyone in it. If you are constantly with the same people, and they are stuck, unsupportive, or negative, you are not part of a group that supports you or brings you opportunities, and you can't help them, either. It's time to meet some new people.

It might seem weird to ask for help or advice from someone you don't know, but I'll tell you a secret: Successful people want to help other people.

It might seem weird to ask for help or advice from someone you don't know, but I'll tell you a secret: Successful people *want* to help other people. That's part of how they got successful—someone else helped them. I think a lot of people don't know that. They also want to help others skip having to take the long route when they can get there more quickly. They want to help others keep from making the mistakes they did—what they lost money or time by doing. Why else would I be writing this book? I want to help you, and I've never even met you!

That's why it's important to recognize that teachers and professionals are looking for people with the same commitment they have. They were starting out once, too, and they know how it feels. Most successful people are happy to answer questions and explain what worked for them. They know it's up to you whether you take the advice or not, but if they see that you are listening and taking their advice, they will want to take you under their wing and help you even more. They're dedicated to the field they love, and they want to bring more good people into it.

So don't feel like a "leech" when you're asking somebody for help. You have nothing to lose! They will either help, or they won't. It's always worth a try.

Who should you talk to? Think of some people you know who are successful in their own fields. Try to surround yourself with them. Ask to take them out for a cup of coffee as your treat just to have a chat for general advice, or try to get in their friend group. Find people who are successful in the work you want to do, and ask them more specific questions about how they approached their careers.

The help goes both ways, too. Though you may not be able to help others when you're just starting out, once you're successful, you can and will. Success is partly about who you know, but also about being there for people who need you, too.

With every interaction, you are creating and reinforcing your network. When your network is a team of people all working to help each other, your whole world is different. Once I started living in this simple mindset, my life completely changed. More opportunities came my way. I got offered jobs—like the position as a laser trainer. I found new business partners to work with. I started trading my own services with other people to help build my business.

And everyone you know is potentially on that team. I have hired people who waitressed or went to school with me.

I remember everything about friends or acquaintances who might fit in that team, and I still think of reaching out to people I haven't talked to in a long time when I hear of opportunities they might be interested in. Being on good terms with all the good people you know is crucial. You will at some point cross paths again, and you never know who is able to help you with something in your life—just like they never know when you'll be able to help them.

Pro Tip: You're Always Networking

Every person you meet may be able to help you in ways you don't even know. They may know people you'd like to get to know, or work at places where you'd also like to work. Your instructors are all potential referrals to job offers in the future, and so are your classmates.

If you've stayed in touch with a former classmate who lands a great job at a place that has another opening for someone with your skills, they're more likely to pass the info along to you and put in a good word if you've kept a good professional relationship with them from the start. If you behave professionally to everyone, and show you're a hard worker, they will be far more likely to recommend you for jobs—and that also works the other way, too. You create or remove opportunities for yourself or others with your actions.

CHAPTER 7

After Graduation— the $40K+ Calendar

WHAT IF YOUR CALENDAR WAS FULL OF APPOINTMENTS that will bring in at least $40K of income for you each year? I say "at least" because that's actually a low figure.

No, really. I'm not kidding.

Yes, it's time to bring up a scary topic again: marketing.

If you're anxious about marketing, you're in good company. It's one of the worries my students express most in the beginning.

The problem is that there's an idea of marketing, and then there's actual marketing. The concept of marketing usually brings up some horrible mental picture of cold-calling people who hang up or yell at you for bothering them. It may feel like you'll be standing on a street corner, handing out flyers to busy strangers to convince someone—anyone—to buy something they don't really want.

Real marketing is nothing like that. In fact, you already do it every day.

If you don't believe me, think about this. When was the last time you saw a movie you loved or ate great food at a restaurant? Did you tell people about them? Or how about someone you met and instantly clicked with—did you want to introduce them to your other friends who would like them, too?

That's marketing.

We are constantly marketing others' products and services. We do it without even thinking. When you're excited about something, you want to tell people about it. If you're excited about the fantastic results your services can bring, shouldn't you let people know about them? Why are you keeping them a secret?

Three Sample Marketing Strategies

At MedSpa Institute of America, we have built a lot of expertise on the best marketing strategies to help you get going quickly. We teach these within our program. Below are just a few examples.

Five Key Points Ad

One thing people get wrong in advertising is talking too much about themselves. They want to tell others what great a company they are or how great their products or services are. The problem is that just telling people you're great doesn't mean they're going to believe you instantly. They want to decide that for themselves. So talking about yourself is not a good strategy to get business.

Your marketing should be talking to your clients about themselves, showing that you know what they need or are thinking about.

Instead, your marketing should be talking to your clients about themselves, showing that you know what they need or are thinking about. What kind of results do they want that you can give? You have to get into their minds.

A Five-Key-Points Ad is a simple way to do that. It includes five crucial (key) pieces of information (points you want to make). In the first four points, you want to make sure you're talking about your product or service. Then, in the last point, you can mention something they need to know—a discount, your location, etc.

For example, in an ad for laser hair removal, I would list four reasons the client might need the service and add a last point about myself that will appeal to or help them. My five key points might look like this:

- Are you embarrassed about unwanted hair?

- Do you struggle with pain from razor burn?

- Are you the person at the beach who has to wear a skirt because you get such bad ingrowns?

- Do you grow excessive hair?

- If this is you, check out our May laser hair removal sale here at XYZ Company.

You always want the first four points to relate to an emotional topic. Why do they need your service? What feeling do they have that they don't like? The last point is when you get to talk about yourself, or your product or sale, as a solution to their problem.

Smart Ad Placement

By knowing your client, not only will you know how to put the right things in the ad, but you'll also understand the right places to put the ad where they will see it. To figure this out, you need to know the answers to other questions:

- Where does this client hang out?

- What does he/she think about every day?

- What does he/she enjoy?

- Can you advertise in those places? If so, what format would be best?

Of course, when thinking about places, you'll want to think about social media. However, the people who go above and beyond the usual Facebook and Instagram ads are the ones who end up super busy and booked out. So getting up and driving to check out actual physical locations where your client goes will help you get a more extensive clientele than just relying on social media.

When you are in the location, you'll see the best options and how to take advantage of them. For instance, in one place, you may want to ask the owner or manager to let you set out brochures or business cards, but another area might have a public bulletin board where you can post your services on a single-sheet flyer. You might even do the strip of tear-off contact information tabs at the bottom for people to take. You wouldn't want to post a brochure on a bulletin board because it wouldn't display well if it's folded or people can only see one unfolded side. If they have to take it down to read it, it will get lost or taken or be too much trouble to bother with.

Tips for Understanding Your Client

So how do you get to know your client? One secret is to think of someone specific who you know—not just "a woman" or "a woman with money." It can be an imaginary person built from several people you know in that category or a real person who you think of as your "ideal" client in a specific group. (You might have more than one ideal client, too.)

Now, start thinking about what things/people this person is extremely passionate about. What do they like? Not like? What do they want? Build a picture of the person in your head. When you're writing ads or marketing materials, write them to this specific person, real or imaginary. Doing this will make it much easier to come up with successful ideas and wording.

Write a Sample Ad

Now is your chance to practice your own ad. Let's do an example of a mom as an ideal client.

Where does this mom hang out? _____

_____

_____

What kinds of advertising could you put there? _____

_____

_____

What kinds of skin-related or general cosmetic concerns might she have, especially being a mom? (Hint: Stretch marks are a top issue.) What might she not have time to do that would affect her? What might she worry about?_____

_____

_____

What four points could you use for a skin-care procedure ad that would appeal to a mom with some of these problems?

1. _____

2. _____

3. _____

4. _____

What kind of thing would you offer her specifically about your company that would make her more likely to contact you—a sale, area of specialization, or other?

5. _____

Once you start looking around, you'll realize that there are advertising opportunities everywhere.

MedSpa Institute's marketing program gives you many great ideas for getting and keeping clients—including tips for marketing to wealthier people that are so secret we can't put them in the book because we want to give our students a competitive edge!

Armed with some background knowledge and good tools to help you, you will feel like a pro at marketing and advertising.

Relationship Marketing

If you're in a position where you already have a clientele, even if they are not medical skin-care clients, you can use marketing to strengthen and build on those relationships.

For instance, say you are a hairdresser. The great news is that you can bring the same clientele into your laser or skin-care practice. You don't have to throw away years of work building those client relationships. Many people often work part-time at their old job while transitioning into their new focus in medical skin care. That, of course, is totally up to you.

The more things you can offer, the more you can help your clients and make a better income.

Succeeding Against All Odds

I had a student from another country, and she and her family traveled all around the US because her husband was a traveling doctor. She did not know anybody in the states, and as soon as she got to know local people, she would have to move. Therefore, her one hesitation with going to school in medical esthetics was her fear of not finding clients.

She attended my marketing class and took everything I said very seriously, trying all my techniques. She had the most people come in for treatments! To this day, she has more clients than anybody I have seen. She also has the most quotas ever achieved by any student in the school—and she truly knew nobody in this state!

She used Facebook, garage sale apps, different neighborhood apps, and others. They all worked well for her. During appointments, she would also ask her clients if they knew anybody who could help her finish her quotas, explaining that she didn't know anyone. People were more than happy to help, especially at the price point of the school. Because she did so well at bringing people in, it inspired her to have her own business even while she travels, and she has continued to get new clients as she goes to new states. She now has a different view of becoming successful and is thankful for what she has learned. She's one of my favorite students to this day. I am so extremely proud of her!

Determining Your Pay Types

When it comes to getting paid, you need to know whether you'll be able to get clients in quickly (and therefore do fine on just flat commission) or if you need to start with an hourly pay rate as a cushion until you get a steady clientele. Flat commission (a specific percentage of everything you sell, say 20 percent) is the most lucrative option for you and your employer.

In an hourly pay situation, if you do a $2K laser hair removal, you only get paid your hourly rate (say $18/hour), and your employer keeps the rest of the $2K you brought in. That would seem like the best scenario for your employer. However, they actually prefer paying commission because it gives you the incentive to sell more.

The downside with a flat commission is that if you don't have clients, you aren't making any money. That's why some people who are starting out feel more comfortable just getting an hourly rate to be guaranteed some income. The most common payment agreement is a hybrid situation with a low hourly rate and low commission. Many start on this and eventually move to just flat commission. With good sales, even a low commission can exceed your flat hourly rate.

If you do start out with only an hourly rate, negotiate a higher rate because no matter how much you sell, you're never going to make more in that job than that starting rate.

It can be scary on flat commission since, without clients, you won't make any money,

It can be scary on flat commission since, without clients, you won't make any money, but don't worry—we offer our students lots of great social media, advertising, and networking tips for generating quick business.

but don't worry—we offer our students lots of great social media, advertising, and networking tips for generating quick business. Follow them correctly, and in a normal market, slow times won't last long!

Appealing to Prospective Employers

By following a couple of simple tips, you'll be a lot more likely to get a job.

First, as with any job application, try to learn as much as possible about the company. What is their main clientele like? What services do they offer? What hours do they hold? What kind of work culture do they have? How would you fit in there, and what kind of expectations would they have for the particular job you're applying for? What kind of experience could you get by working there? Who are their staff, and what are their credentials and training? This will help you give educated answers about what you might bring to them with your skills.

Second, how you apply will say a lot about your qualifications. Unlike some situations on the beauty side, applying for medical esthetics jobs is similar to the way a nurse would apply for a job. He or she wouldn't walk into a hospital and hand a resume to the front desk. As a medical esthetician, you also would not walk in and hand the front desk your resume. If you're not applying to an ad for a specific job but want them to have your resume on file, it's best to call and find out who is in charge of hiring for your type of position. Then you can send your resume directly to that person, along with a cover letter telling them why you're interested in working there. Most jobs don't even post online—they're filled through networking. That's why it's so important to build a great network.

Pro Tip: Have the Full Package

One of my students did all three types of training available at MedSpa Institute: esthetics, advanced practice esthetics, and laser certification. She landed a beautiful job at graduation and has been there ever since, getting better and better at it.

But her success isn't just because she has all three credentials; she's also highly professional and works hard. The full package is vital. If you work hard and are professional but aren't trained, you won't get into your dream job. But if your great credentials land you a dream job and you don't work hard and keep a professional attitude, you may not keep it long.

Also, be ready to answer detailed questions about medical esthetics and equipment. When I was a regular esthetician trying to get into lasers with no training. I managed to get an interview, only to have them ask me questions I could not answer. For instance, they asked what my favorite laser was, which laser manufacturer I like best, and how I would treat a patient who had a weird reaction. This was when I realized I was simply not qualified. And so did the interviewer. Managers can easily tell when somebody does not have experience.

CHAPTER 8

Financing Your Education

ONE SIGNIFICANT WORRY MANY STUDENTS HAVE is how to pay for school. However, it's easier than you think to plan your finances—and the best part is that you don't have to figure it all out all alone. A good school will help and support you in different ways, whether that means helping you work out the costs and find financial aid or letting you block out your time to work and earn a living while you're in school.

For instance, at MedSpa Institute of America, we have created ways for you to earn a living faster and while getting the skills to become a medical laser technician.

Starting at the Beginning: Your Goals

During the informational tour, we spend a lot of time with prospective students. We will talk about your goals, your dream job, why you're deciding now is the time. We want to

Some things may surprise you on your tour. The more information you have, the more ideas you'll have for what you want to do.

know your true "why"—why are you choosing this for your career? How is this going to change your family's life? How will this career fulfill your day-to-day happiness? How will this field allow you to help other people?

We don't just want to know your goals; we want to help you achieve them.

Once we understand who you are and what you want to accomplish, we will give you a personalized education plan to help you do it. There is a reason we don't have an "apply" button on our website—we want to truly make sure this is worth your time and money. It's not a "one-size-fits-all" process because every person is unique. We care so much about your path that we want to meet you in person. (If you are from another state and traveling is challenging, we can have a phone conversation).

We encourage everybody to have their main life decision-maker(s) present for the tour. These could be parents, a life partner, or another significant person in your life. They need to be there when we talk through all these goals so they can support you in your decision-making.

Some things may surprise you on your tour. The more information you have, the more ideas you'll have for what you want to do. You may find you are interested in something you weren't before because you didn't know enough about it.

Question: Before you read the next section, jot down a quick answer here. From 1-10, with 10 being highest and 1 being lowest, how worried are you about paying for school?_____

_____

_____

Think Long-Term

When we talk through your goals, we focus on long-term vs. short-term thinking. You can achieve even the most impossible-feeling goals in small steps, with every action designed to help bring in more income to support you. We provide examples of jobs you could do during your training with us. People usually are surprised at the variety of options.

For example, say you're passionate about esthetics and want to start with an esthetics course. Most spas are open evenings until 9-9:30 p.m., so while in school, you could also get a student esthetics job and "earn while you learn." After finishing your formal esthetics training, you can get a non-student esthetics job using your new skills at higher pay. For instance, you could work at a wax center or do facials at a gym or a high-end spa. At any of these, you can still stay on the second shift, working evenings and/or weekends while going to school in the mornings.

Once you finish your next training, you can either add that service to the job you're already in or get a new job using the new skills. Each expansion of your menu makes you even more money. This would continue as you stack laser skills with the others and offer them within your same job or move up and get a new job with even higher pay.

Unlike esthetics training, which has daytime courses running for months, the laser course is a two-week intensive course. After that, you have a very flexible internship where you can schedule time around work and school. If you're interested in other things, such as microblading or cosmetic injections, we can stack those on your skill set in the same way.

Here's how this process fast-tracks you into your new career:

- During the whole time, you are learning in school while practicing your career skills in a job that directly relates to your career.

- By working while in school, you're earning money that can help offset your training investment right away.

- Because you practice your skills in your job vs. taking all your courses first and getting a job afterward, you get a quicker return on your learning investment.

- You get better at your job right away because you're getting plenty of experience out in the field even while still in school.

- The whole time, you're building a clientele—and you haven't even finished your courses yet!

Everything is working for you and building on the foundation to create the life you want. You aren't wasting time doing unrelated jobs or taking unwanted courses that don't bring you closer to achieving your goals.

The money would be far less of a problem because you're working the entire time, and the work itself just stacks into your career goals. It's not a random job that isn't related. Everything is working for you and building on the foundation to create the life you want. You aren't wasting time doing unrelated jobs or taking unwanted courses that don't bring you closer to achieving your goals.

Find Creative Solutions

The old saying that you have to spend money to make money is true—but it isn't really "spending." It's actually investing. Investing in yourself is one of the best things you can do. If you make good decisions, the return on your investment will last your entire lifetime.

At MedSpa Institute, we don't just counsel our students about medical esthetics training and business. We also talk about other investment options to help make more money on top of a laser career. Some good ideas include real estate or e-commerce. You can use these within your skin-care company as well.

Investing in yourself is one of the best things you can do. If you make good decisions, the return on your investment will last your entire lifetime.

Maybe your goal would be to make real estate money by owning your building and renting empty space to others. Another goal might be selling your skin-care products on Amazon. The more we know about you, the more ideas we can give. And chances are, we know someone who is doing what you want to do and can give you sound advice on how to get started.

It comes back to your passion and what you really want in your life. It may be having a fun job, or contributing to others' success, or having enough income to explore your art or your creativity. Maybe it's your passion for providing for your family or your desire to prove something to yourself or someone else. Maybe you just want to show your kids what's possible.

If there's something that you really want in life, you will find the money to make it happen. You just need to start thinking about all the different options and find one that will work. Here are some ways our students have paid for their schooling:

- Bank loans

- School-sponsored payment plans (MedSpa Institute offers several options)

- Federal aid through the FAFSA® process (available soon through MedSpa Institute!)

- A loan from a family member or family friend to support the student's career choice

There's always a possibility, and there's always a way.

Follow-up Question: Does the impossible sound a little more possible now? How worried are you about finances now, from 1-10?

_____

_____

_____

If your score is a 6 or higher at this point, schedule a tour with our Admissions team at 952-681-2167, ext. 3. You aren't obligated to apply, and you'll feel better once you look at your own custom plan and have a chance to ask questions.

CHAPTER 9

You're Better Than You Think

WHEN STARTING ANY JOB OR PASSION, all you need is confidence and courage. Success is not about doing the safe thing—it's about taking the risk or the leap of faith to start something new and not giving up until you achieve it.

Everything you've learned about your potential for success is wrong. Don't feel like you must have straight A's growing up your whole life or do well on the SAT or ACT. I didn't even take those tests, knowing I wouldn't go to college—yet I'm a successful businessperson. You can be, too!

Be the Right Kind of Smart

Don't get me wrong: You need intelligence to be successful. However, the more important part of intelligence doesn't have much to do with books and memorizing facts you'll never use. Instead, it comes down to managing your life. You need goals and a strategy to succeed, and you need to know where you are within those. You need to understand how to handle business responsibilities and help create a positive culture that works for everyone. When you find something you're interested in, these come naturally.

It's also intelligent to know yourself and what you genuinely need to do at any point. Sometimes that means knowing when to give up. If you're not ready to learn something and you have no interest in it, don't waste time and money trying to force yourself to do it at that time. Though you think you *should* do something because you feel pressured for some reason, that doesn't mean you should actually *do* it. When I forced myself to try to get a two-year degree, I dreaded going to school every day as I drove there thinking, "What am I doing with my life?" It wasn't for me. I wasn't afraid. I just didn't want to do it.

Even if you have always been told you're smart and you get good grades, that alone isn't enough to become successful. You have to be smart enough to find something you really want to do, put in the work, and learn a valuable skill set. You also have to know how to sell yourself and your skills to prospective employers (and clients!). These things may sound intimidating, but people who plan and are smart enough not to let their fear of failure make them quit will succeed if they work hard and don't give up.

In my opinion, setting goals and tracking your progress is a huge part of moving forward in life. Take time for yourself, even if it's just five minutes every night, to just check in and think about how your day went, what you learned from it, what you need to get done

> *Even if you have always been told you're smart and you get good grades, that alone isn't enough to become successful. You have to be smart enough to find something you really want to do, put in the work, and learn a valuable skill set.*

tomorrow. It doesn't have to be something significant—it could be anything, even personal tasks like "I'm finally going to fold that laundry tomorrow!" Or you can make a note that someone at work doesn't seem happy, and you're going to compliment them tomorrow or treat them to lunch. Or maybe you feel you and your life partner have become distant, and you want to show them some love.

These are simple things. It doesn't always have to be about work.

If we don't take time to focus on these things, it's hard to grow and move forward in life.

But doing it will help you become the "you" that you want to be or help you figure out who that "you" is. Self-development is key.

Value Yourself

Never devalue your skills. Everyone has something to contribute. If you're not sure what your strengths and abilities are, ask. Ask your closest friends and your family to tell you what they think your best qualities are. Have them write down their answers so you can look at them when you are frustrated.

For a long time, I was embarrassed that I wasn't good at school. Whenever people would ask, "What college are you going to?" I'd just change the subject.

Today, instead of being embarrassed about my shortcomings, I'm focused on and grateful for my skills, which got me where I am now.

For instance, I can speak in front of hundreds of people, and I know many people would not be comfortable doing that. I figured out how to run a business because I got good advice and followed it, but I also had good problem-solving skills and a lot of common sense.

Remember, you can use your strengths to overcome or downplay your weaknesses. Even being the traditional idea of "smart" can be a weakness for some people in some situations. For instance, teamwork can be frustrating for very intelligent people.[24] Sometimes, they just want to work by themselves to get something done because they believe no one else can do it quickly or well enough. But working together is how you move forward in life, and most work situations require teamwork. This is one of the most important strengths for success, whether you are a business owner or an employee/coworker.

Also, highly intelligent people can often overthink things. What if you constantly think about every little thing that could go wrong in every situation? Would you actually ever make a decision? Probably not—but this is another pit many people fall into.

I had a student who was terribly shy. Not only that, but being a male, he worried no one would hire him in the female-dominated medical esthetics industry. But, to his surprise, he got snapped up immediately out of school. Employers wanted him because he was certified to do laser treatments along with handling massage and spa clients. He found confidence by doing something he loves and focusing on it instead of his fear.

What If Everything Goes Well?

Instead of fearing the worst, if you contemplate everything that could go right, you'll have a totally different view of the new life ahead of you.

---

24   Alice Boyes, "Five Ways Smart People Sabotage Their Success," *Harvard Business Review*, November 13, 2018, https://hbr.org/2018/11/5-ways-smart-people-sabotage-their-success

Whenever I share my story with classes full of students, so many people relate to the things I'm telling you right now. Many didn't know what they wanted to do in life or felt they weren't good or smart enough. Many attempted college but found it wasn't for them.

I'll tell you another secret: Just the fact I'm writing a book is crazy to me. But I wanted to challenge myself with something I knew I wouldn't be good at, and here I am! This was one of my own goals, and I'm going to finish it and check it off my list!

If doing the thing you fear pushes you to become successful in your career or to gain confidence, I challenge you to face it head-on.

Be Enough in Your Own Eyes

A talk I once had with Dr. Tholen, who is one of my mentors, made an impression on me. I said, "Some people think I'm too young to do what I'm doing, and they can't be happy for me. Or maybe they wouldn't trust me, or they're just genuinely confused about how I could build the business I have created."

He said, "Carly, you know that you're never enough for some people, and you can't worry about what they think." He went on to explain, "People say to me that I'm too old; that I shouldn't be doing surgery anymore. But I'm perfectly capable of doing surgery, and I have years ahead of me."

I had another conversation with a friend years before. She is an MD. I asked her if she thought I should go back and get my RN degree to be "more credible." She said, "You know what, Carly? I am a medical doctor, and I am not enough to some people because I am a woman. You're never going to be enough in some people's eyes, and you just have to brush it off."

Now, I'm past that. I can just hire a nurse if I need a nurse for my business. I don't need to put in the time, effort, and money when I'm not going to use it. Honestly, I would have had to work more hours to make the same or less income that I was already making by working as a laser-certified esthetician. It's not that I'm afraid to go back to school. It's actually funny because I know that if I wanted to go to nursing school, I would be good at it because I have taught myself that I do like school after all—if I'm doing something I want to do.

Knowledge and skill are what people want. If you take yourself seriously, your clients will also take you seriously, which means they will trust your skills and recommendations. If you have the confidence to grab a piece of high-tech laser equipment and know exactly what to do with it, your team of nurses and doctors will respect you.

If you take yourself seriously, your clients will also take you seriously, which means they will trust your skills and recommendations.

If you want to make a difference in your life, and you're ready to do it, the universe will give you all the tools to become successful at it and put you in the right spot. Hopefully, that spot will be somewhere like MedSpa Institute of America, where your instructors can guide you into your new career and give you everything you need. We will never send you into the world unprepared! We've got your back.

CHAPTER 10

What Matters Most to You?

WHEN I STARTED THIS CAREER, I had a lot of luck and help figuring out what I wanted to do. Some of the steps I took were just looking for the right move to make. I wasted a lot of time and money on the wrong decisions. But when I figured it all out, it changed my life.

By now, you've absorbed a lot of information from this book. So let's take a few minutes to think through what you now know:

1. You know I succeeded though I wasn't a great student in high school.

2. You know there's a lot more information and help in the industry now than when I started out.

3. You know that if you listen to my advice, you won't have to make the mistakes I did.

4. You know what a tremendous opportunity is waiting. You've even done the numbers to look at the income possibilities for yourself. (If you skipped that part, go back and do it now, or you will never know what you missed.)

5. You have a great idea now what medical esthetics careers you can get into and how.

6. You know something about the coursework and what it looks like.

7. You have some ideas for making the finances work—stacking your skills, working in your field to boost your experience while in school, and more.

8. You have some tips for being a top student and rocking your training.

9. You know how to market yourself to clients, your network, and potential employers. I've even shown you how to think about your strengths and weaknesses in a way that will make you shine.

You have all the right tools to make your game-changing decision to jump into this lucrative skin-care business. This isn't the time to hesitate or procrastinate.

Every day you wait, your future is delayed more. Remember my student who wasted sixteen months trying to find an alternate route when she could have been in her new career in just a couple of months? Don't make that mistake.

Before I started on this path, all my friends were going to college, and I was still at home with my parents. Between waitressing and driving to whatever friends' college party was going on that weekend, I had plenty to do, but I had no plan for myself. I felt lost. I was going nowhere. To fill my time, I would waitress double shifts all day, every day.

Now I have a certain sense of freedom knowing where my career is headed; I know that I am done with work at dinner time; I know this career will never die. I'm highly comfortable with being in medical esthetics, knowing this is going to be needed forever. Everybody ages and everybody is going to want to look younger and more attractive.

It's About What's Best for You

Don't let other people's doubts change your mind about your dreams.

One potential student who toured with me was very standoff-ish, yet she seemed to want to attend our school. She was actually quite rude to me during the conversation. I wrote in her chart that if she wanted to sign up, I would need to be the one to meet with her one on one again and let her know I felt like we needed one more conversation to make sure this was a right fit.

I was surprised when she called back to sign up. When she returned, she was a completely different person. She immediately apologized and said, "I know I was rude to you in my tour, and I want you to know I was in a really bad place in my life. But this is my dream, and it's what I want to do." Then she explained that her husband had not approved of her starting this new career, and that's where her rudeness came from. She had since divorced him and was ready to start this chapter in her new life.

Only you know within your heart what you're meant to do.

I'm not advocating divorce, but even the people closest to you can keep you from doing something you really want to do. It's up to you to weigh things in a new way to figure it all out. Only you know within your heart what you're meant to do. Sometimes the people closest to you are scared for you, or afraid you'll fail, or afraid you'll succeed and won't have time for them! These things might make you hold back—but you need to push through that with compassion. You don't need permission for your life; you are in control of your destiny. Don't let anyone take that away from you, even when they mean well.

Don't Just Take My Word for It

Whether you are young and figuring out your new job or career, or this is a second career, and you plan on retiring with it, it's a great plan either way. But you don't have to take my word for it. Here are some things our students have said about our program.

> *"I am currently a laser student at this school, and I love my experience! I would not trade it for anything else in this world!"*

> *"Going to MedSpa Institute of America was one of the best things I've ever done in my life. The training gave me the confidence to start my own business. I had never done anything in this industry until then, and I took off running after I completed school. Carly was my instructor at the time, and I learned so much! I'm forever grateful for the opportunity. I immediately started my own business, and it has grown very quickly."*

> *"After esthetics training at another school, I landed a job at a medspa, and even though I had been provided 'training' at the job for the laser devices, I still had questions*

that were unanswered. I felt so lost and not confident, and I was not willing to risk my licensure and reputation by hurting clients. This is one reason why I decided to take this course."

"This has only been my third day of laser training, and I have learned so much! This laser program is amazing because of how much hands-on experience you get. You learn how to adjust the device settings to match each skin type so you don't hurt clients, and so you can get maximum results. You also learn how to create a skin plan and add in your expertise to help clients get to their skin goals, which is a real-life lesson that will build your clientele."

"Laser class sizes are quite small, and I love the one-on-one time you get with the instructor. The instructors are so knowledgeable and easy to work with. Also, I want to say that the school has handled COVID safely. I love the fact that this school is so diverse in every way. We get to work with different ethnic backgrounds and different skin conditions. This school also combines different programs. Sometimes we work with students from other programs to fully understand different types of skin lesions and the medical terminology. It's learning in a real-life setting and works even for visual learners. I'm a licensed advanced practice esthetician, and I found that this laser course also helped me understand skin with a whole other perspective. In addition, this school is welcoming to all genders."

"Just being here, I have learned how to chart, how to market, how to handle different devices, what clinical endpoints should look like, etc."

"Overall, if you're looking for a laser school or are interested in a laser program, I would recommend this school. Not only do you get the most bang for your buck, but you also learn so many new and updated modalities. I already feel prepared and ready to further my career!!! At the end of your schooling, no one stays a stranger. We all support each other. BTW, CARLY IS AMAZING! ♡"

"Just finished classes for Luxury Laser and it was the best experience and decision EVER!! I love that the class sizes are small and that we all get hands-on experience with all the systems and treatments, which is the best way to learn. The teachers and staff are amazing—so friendly, supportive, and helpful through the entire duration. I would definitely recommend this to everyone who is looking for a change in career paths or looking for an exciting new career start. This has been an all-around great experience, and I cannot wait to see what the future holds."

"MedSpa Institute of America is a great institution with amazing staff!! I attended the laser class and felt comfortable performing all treatments by the end of the program. It is very hands-on, which helps with retaining information, as you will learn a lot in a short amount of time. I have to say, the other students in my class were fabulous as well!! Highly recommended!!!"

"I really enjoyed my training here. I researched for a long time on laser trainings, and I liked that you learn the most here and that it's licensed! Worth every penny! The teachers were so nice and helpful, and I am so sad class is done. I learned so many things, especially why I couldn't get a job before I had the training. It now all makes sense! I am excited to come in for my internship and practice more hands-on—on actual clients! My only regret is not taking it sooner. I feel extremely accomplished!"

"Attending this school was one of the smartest decisions I made. I felt stuck doing basic facials at my job, and I wanted to advance my skill set. When I read about all the treatments that were taught in the laser course, I knew I had to go for it. I felt confident because I was using the most up-to-date lasers and products, and the instructors are so supportive and eager to help you advance your education. If you want to further your knowledge or make a career change, this program is for you."

"Already being an esthetician, I found that I wanted something a little more. I liked the idea of lasers; the technology is more advanced in skin care, and it just seemed exciting! The training was one of the best decisions I ever made. I learned so many procedures and gained more product knowledge. The class sizes are small, and everything is hands-on. The teachers and staff are amazing. They really do want the best for you! Carly is such an inspiration. Everyone there gave me so much confidence for my future in this industry! I highly recommend this program to anyone!"

"I loved the tangible, hands-on training I received. We worked on state-of-the-art equipment, and the services we learned are in high demand. I have been in the esthetics field for ten years and still learned so much—great training and down-to-earth people, all passionate about the field. The staff is here to help you after class is over, and they extend internship opportunities so you are confident going into your career. I can't wait to dive in for more!"

"Before starting school at MedSpa Institute of America, I was working full-time at a major beauty retailer. I loved working in the beauty industry, but I wanted more in my career. Helping people feel their best will always be something that I love. I had connections to people who were successful in the industry. When I asked about the best school to pursue this career, MedSpa Institute of America was always highly recommended.

"Fast forward nine months, and I have completed both the esthetician and the advanced practice esthetician courses. While attending the school, I've had many employers reach out to me, impressed with the social media marketing skills that the school has taught me. I will never regret my decision to take courses at this school. It has taught me so much and helped me build my confidence and knowledge in the beauty industry even further."

CHAPTER 11

Take the First Step

SO, IF YOU'RE STILL WITH ME, you probably agree that medical esthetics is a great career. Now, how do you make it happen?

It probably won't surprise you that I encourage you to apply to MedSpa Institute of America. Here's how to do that:

1. Schedule a Visit!
The first step will be to **contact Admissions** to schedule your tour.

- **Phone: 952-681-2167 ext. 3**

- **Email: info@medspatrainingusa.com**

- Don't forget to include your decision-makers in the scheduling process—you'll want them to be there, too.

2. Prepare for Your Tour
Before your tour, you'll want to have a few things ready.

- Write down at least a general idea of your career goals and the esthetics courses you're interested in, so you're ready to talk them through with our staff.

- Be sure to talk to your decision-makers or influencers beforehand so they know why you're interested in the program. Tell them your goals, too, so that they know what you want to do and why.

- Write down all the questions you and your decision-makers have so you don't forget anything while you're with us.

3. During Your Tour

On your tour day, be ready to spend a few hours with us. During that time, we'll do the following:

- Take you on a walkthrough of the facilities so you can see our classrooms and meet some of the staff.

- Discuss your goals, why you're interested in the program, and where you'd like to be in the future.

- Go over your financial questions and look at strategies for building your income during school.

- Put together your personalized education plan, complete with the strategy for stacking your training to continue building your income as you work through school.

- Discuss options for how you'd like to pay for school.

- Give you ideas for building your business and creating other income streams while you're working out in the field after graduation.

- Provide a packet of information for you to take home.

4. Enrolling

After the tour, you can sign up for the next class or get on a waiting list. All you have to do is put your kit fee down whenever you're ready to hold your spot.

Once you've enrolled, you'll get a series of helpful emails telling you what's next, including your schedule, where you can eat, how to get your uniforms, how you'll access the coursework, and much more.

One Last Tip

My biggest suggestion is that whatever skin-care route you take, add laser training to it. Years ago, hair salons did not have spas, and now pretty much every hair salon has a spa. Now many of those spas are turning into medical spas. To keep up with the competition, you're going to need to get the credentials that everybody else has.

If someone has laser certification and someone else doesn't, an employer is going to hire the one with laser certification—even over a nurse.

We Can't Wait to Meet You!

I love to see my students on social media, showing where they're working, proudly displaying their menus, saying they're booked out. I couldn't be happier for them or prouder of them. And I know you can join that group too and experience everything they have.

I look at my daughter, and I think how blessed our life is and that I wouldn't have this life if I hadn't gone into medical esthetics. Being able to get a head start on my career while my friends were still in college has been a huge blessing and allowed me to support my husband and his dreams, too.

I can put my daughter in dance or whatever sports she wants to be in. I can provide for my family but also know that if I was by myself, I could take care of myself as well. I don't need to depend on somebody else.

You can do these things, too. You have the advantage of getting into this booming industry starting right now! So what are you waiting for? Every day you wait is a lost day of your new life.

We can't wait to meet you and start you down this amazing path!

Thank You

FIRST, I WANT TO THANK MY HUSBAND, BRAD, for supporting me in writing this book through my pregnancy with Eden. He is a helpful reminder that anything is possible.

I also want to thank my dad, Mike, for the important life lessons he taught me, including the value of a solid work ethic.

I would also like to thank my staff at MedSpa Institute of America, who work hard every day to help students succeed in this incredible field. In particular, I want to express my gratitude to our medical director, Dr. Richard Tholen, who has been a wonderful mentor to me through the years.

In addition, I'd like to thank all our current and former students for allowing me to be part of their success. I am so proud of them and the incredible things they do for their clients, each other, and our industry every day.

You all rock!

About the Author

CARLY WILLIAMS GREW UP IN BURNSVILLE, MINNESOTA. Dance was her primary identity until she found her love for skin care. Carly is a licensed esthetician and a licensed esthetics instructor and also has her laser certification.

Due to the lack of available information and formal training when she began her career, Carly found it challenging to get started. So, to improve the experience for others, she designed a course to train people to properly perform laser treatments. Carly eventually opened the first laser and injection school in Minnesota/the Midwest. In addition, she was responsible for creating the laser certification and licensing requirements for the state of Minnesota. Over the years, Carly's original training program grew and evolved. Today, it is the premiere institution known as MedSpa Institute of America, of which Carly is owner and president.

Throughout her career, Carly has helped countless people succeed in the laser and medspa industry. She works side-by-side with RNs and doctors as national trainers for lasers and many advanced modalities. She was asked to be an official laser trainer for Candela, the Midwest Territory for Plasma Pen, and BB Glow Academy. She travels across the United States and Australia, speaking and demonstrating advanced skin-care techniques as well as self-love and empowerment.

In addition to her work travels, she also loves to travel for fun with her husband, Brad, their daughter, Eden, and their Aussiedoodle, Tinley.

Schedule an Appearance

To arrange a speaking engagement or book tour with Carly at your beauty school or other organization, please reach out to MedSpa Institute of America.

Phone: (952) 681-2167
Email: **info@medspatrainingusa.com**
Website: **Luxurylaseredu.com**

Made in the USA
Middletown, DE
15 February 2022

61140646R00064